Unit 1: Living with the Physical

Unit 1A — Tectonic Hazards

Page 4: Tectonic Plates

1.1   C *[1 mark]*
       F *[1 mark]*

1.2   At a **destructive** *[1 mark]* plate margin, the two tectonic
       plates are moving towards each other. Where a continental
       plate meets an oceanic plate, the **oceanic** *[1 mark]* plate is
       forced downwards into the mantle. As well as volcanoes, other
       landforms such as **ocean trenches** *[1 mark]* are created by this
       process.

1.3   As the two plates move away from each other, magma (molten
       rock) rises from the mantle to fill the gap *[1 mark]*. It cools,
       creating new crust *[1 mark]*.

Page 5: Volcanoes and Earthquakes

1.1   E.g. volcanoes are most commonly found along destructive
       plate margins, but they also occur at constructive plate margins
       [1 mark]. Some are also found away from plate margins, e.g. in
       Hawaii *[1 mark]*.

1.2   Any one from: e.g. volcanoes are found at destructive margins
       because the oceanic plate moves down into the mantle and
       melts, forming magma *[1 mark]*. This magma rises through
       cracks in the crust (called vents) and erupts at the surface,
       forming volcanoes *[1 mark]*. / Volcanoes are found at
       constructive margins because as the plates pull apart, a gap
       forms between them *[1 mark]*. Magma rises into this gap, and
       erupts at the surface, forming volcanoes *[1 mark]*. / Volcanoes
       are found at hotspots in the Earth's crust where the mantle is
       particularly hot *[1 mark]*. Magma forces its way through the
       crust, forming a volcano *[1 mark]*.

2.1   Almost all earthquakes are found along plate margins *[1 mark]*
       but some (very few) occur in the middle of plates *[1 mark]*.

2.2   Tension builds up as one plate gets stuck as it moves down past
       the other into the mantle *[1 mark]*. The plates eventually jerk
       past each other *[1 mark]*, sending out shockwaves *[1 mark]*.

Pages 6-7: Tectonic Hazards — Effects and Responses

1.1   Volcanic eruptions — any two from: e.g. buildings are destroyed
       by lava flows *[1 mark]*. / People are injured or killed by falling
       debris *[1 mark]*. / Buildings collapse if enough ash falls on them
       [1 mark]. / Crops are damaged when ash falls on them *[1 mark]*.
       Earthquakes — any two from: e.g. Buildings are destroyed by
       ground shaking *[1 mark]*. / Roads are damaged or destroyed
       [1 mark]. / Electricity cables and communications networks are
       damaged, cutting off supplies *[1 mark]*.

1.2   Volcanic eruptions — any two from: e.g. eruptions can trigger
       mudflows and landslides, which cause more destruction and
       death *[1 mark]*. / Transport networks are blocked or destroyed
       so aid and emergency vehicles can't get through, and trade is
       difficult *[1 mark]*. / Damaged or destroyed businesses cause
       unemployment and loss of income *[1 mark]*. / Recovering
       after an eruption can be very expensive, weakening a country's
       economy *[1 mark]*.
       Earthquakes — any two from: e.g. people who are left homeless
       could die, e.g. from cold *[1 mark]*. / There's a shortage of clean
       water and a lack of proper sanitation — this makes it easier
       for diseases to spread *[1 mark]*. / Due to blocked or destroyed
       roads, aid and emergency vehicles can't get through, and trade
       is difficult *[1 mark]*. / Businesses are damaged or destroyed,
       causing unemployment and lost income *[1 mark]*. / Repairs
       and reconstruction can be very expensive, which can weaken a
       country's economy *[1 mark]*.

1.3   Any two from: e... areas, so tectoni...
       [1 mark]. / Urba...
       areas; if these are ... , the economic cost of the hazard will
       be higher *[1 mark]*. / There are more buildings in urban areas,
       which can collapse on people, causing injuries and fatalities
       [1 mark].

2.1   E.g. Hazard B occurred in a high-income country, which would
       have had more money available to evacuate people from the area
       [1 mark], so fewer people would have been killed as the hazard
       struck *[1 mark]*.

2.2   Any two from: e.g. rescue people trapped by collapsed buildings
       [1 mark]. / Treat injured people *[1 mark]*. / Recover dead bodies
       to prevent spread of disease *[1 mark]*. / Put out fires *[1 mark]*.
       / Set up temporary shelters for people whose homes have been
       damaged or destroyed *[1 mark]*. / Provide water, food, electricity
       and gas for people who have been affected *[1 mark]*.

2.3   This question is level marked. How to grade your answer:
       Level 0:   There is no relevant information. *[0 marks]*
       Level 1:   There is a basic explanation of why the long-term
                   death toll is likely to be higher in a low-income
                   country. *[1-2 marks]*
       Level 2:   There is a detailed explanation of why the
                   long-term death toll is likely to be higher in a
                   low-income country. *[3-4 marks]*
       Here are some points your answer may include:
       • Hazard A occurred in a low-income country, which may
         not have been able to afford effective long-term responses
         to the hazard, whereas the high-income country in which
         Hazard B occurred would have been better able to afford
         long-term responses.
       • For example, rehousing homeless people may have taken a
         long time in the area affected by Hazard A, so people may
         have died, e.g. from exposure to cold weather.
       • There may not have been money to repair roads and
         transport systems in the area affected by Hazard A, which
         would have made it difficult for aid and medical care to
         reach those affected.
       • It may have taken a long time to repair damaged water and
         sewage systems, meaning that people may not have had
         access to clean water. This would have caused disease to
         spread, increasing the death toll.

2.4   Hazard B had a much higher economic impact than Hazard A,
       costing four times as much to rebuild the area affected *[1 mark]*.

2.5   E.g. the buildings and roads that are damaged in a high-income
       country tend to be made from more expensive materials than
       those in a low-income country *[1 mark]*, so they cost a more
       money to rebuild *[1 mark]*.

2.6   This question is level marked. There are 3 extra marks
       available for spelling, punctuation and grammar.
       How to grade your answer:
       Level 0:   There is no relevant information. *[0 marks]*
       Level 1:   There is a basic description of responses to tectonic
                   hazards in two different areas. *[1-3 marks]*
       Level 2:   There is a clear comparison of responses to tectonic
                   hazards in two different areas and an assessment of
                   how effective they were. *[4-6 marks]*
       Level 3:   There is a detailed comparison of multiple
                   responses to tectonic hazards in two different areas,
                   and a detailed assessment of how the responses
                   altered the effects of the hazards. *[7-9 marks]*
       Make sure your spelling, punctuation and grammar is
       consistently correct, that your meaning is clear and that you use
       a range of geographical terms correctly *[0-3 marks]*.
       Your answer should refer to two named examples.
       Here are some points your answer may include:
       • A brief description of hazards in both countries — when
         they happened, where they happened and what happened.

Answers

Unit 1: Living with the Physical Environment

- A comparison of the immediate responses to the hazard in the two countries affected, such as emergency shelter, food and water for the people affected, and how this increased or decreased the impacts of the hazard.
- A comparison of the long-term responses to the hazard in the two countries affected, such as rebuilding the affected area and building new settlements, and how this increased or decreased the impacts of the hazard.
- Answers may refer to New Zealand (Kaikoura earthquake in 2016) and Nepal (Gorkha earthquake in 2015). In New Zealand, effective immediate responses, such as evacuating people, limited the death toll to 2 people, and water and electricity supplies were re-established rapidly. In Nepal, rescue efforts were hampered by a lack of tools, aid took a long time to reach the affected area, and it took several years for water supply to be restored to some areas. This contributed to a death toll of approximately 9000.

Page 8: Living With Tectonic Hazards

1.1 Any two from: e.g. lots of tourists are likely to visit Mount Fuji, so people may live in the area to work in the tourist industry *[1 mark]*. / Yokohama is a busy city with lots of businesses, so lots of people are employed there *[1 mark]*. / The buildings look very modern, so they may have been built to withstand hazards, therefore people may believe they will be safe if an earthquake or eruption occurs *[1 mark]*. / People may believe that a severe earthquake or eruption won't happen again in the area *[1 mark]*.

1.2 This question is level marked. How to grade your answer:
Level 0: There is no relevant information. *[0 marks]*
Level 1: There is a basic description of one or two building features. *[1-2 marks]*
Level 2: There is a clear description of specific building features and an explanation of how they might help to reduce the effects of tectonic hazards. *[3-4 marks]*
Here are some points your answer may include:
- Buildings, bridges etc. might have been designed to withstand earthquakes, e.g. by using materials like reinforced concrete or building special foundations that absorb an earthquake's energy.
- Existing buildings and bridges might have been strengthened (e.g. by wrapping pillars in steel frames) so they're less likely to collapse under the weight of falling ash or due to shaking from an earthquake.
- Adaptations like these would make buildings less likely to collapse during a tectonic hazard, so fewer people would be killed, injured or trapped. Also, less rebuilding would be necessary, so the economic effects would be reduced.
- Automatic shut-off switches can turn off gas and electricity supplies if an earthquake is detected by a monitoring system. This prevents fires and therefore reduces the death toll and damage to the city.

1.3 This question is level marked. How to grade your answer:
Level 0: There is no relevant information. *[0 marks]*
Level 1: There is a basic description of one or two planning strategies. *[1-2 marks]*
Level 2: There is a clear description of several planning strategies and an explanation of how they might help to reduce the effects of tectonic hazards. *[3-4 marks]*
Here are some points your answer may include:
- Future developments can be planned to avoid the areas most at risk from tectonic hazards, so that future hazards affect a smaller area.
- Emergency services can train and prepare for disasters, e.g. by practising rescuing people from collapsed buildings or setting up shelters. This will reduce the number of people killed or injured.

- People can be educated so that they know what to do if an earthquake or eruption happens. This will mean that they know how to respond, so deaths and injuries will be reduced.
- Governments can plan evacuation routes to get people out of dangerous areas quickly and safely in case of an earthquake or volcanic eruption. This reduces the number of people killed or injured by hazards such as fires, pyroclastic flows or mudflows.
- Emergency supplies, like blankets, clean water and food, can be stockpiled. If a natural hazard is predicted, the stockpiles can be moved close to areas likely to be affected, so they are quickly accessible when they are needed.

1.4 E.g. earth movements and volcanoes can be monitored *[1 mark]*, so that people have time to evacuate the area or prepare before an earthquake or eruption occurs *[1 mark]*.

Unit 1A — Weather Hazards

Page 9: Global Atmospheric Circulation

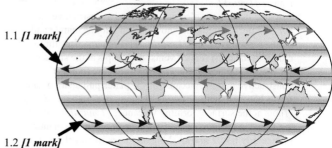

1.1 *[1 mark]*

1.2 *[1 mark]*

1.3 Winds move from areas of **high** *[1 mark]* pressure to areas of **low** *[1 mark]* pressure. Air from the equator rises and moves towards the poles then cools down and sinks at about **30°** *[1 mark]* north and south of the equator.

1.4 C *[1 mark]*

Page 10: Tropical Storms

1.1 Tropical storms form near the equator *[1 mark]*, then move westwards and away from the equator *[1 mark]*.

1.2 E.g. Tropical storms only form over water that's 27 °C or warmer *[1 mark]*. Water is warmest around the equator, so storms form there *[1 mark]*.

1.3 Any two from: e.g. tropical storms have a circular shape *[1 mark]*. / They are hundreds of kilometres wide *[1 mark]*. / Tropical storms have an eye at their centre, which is up to 50 km across *[1 mark]*. / In the eye of the tropical storm, pressure is low and winds are light *[1 mark]*. / There is an eye wall that surrounds the eye *[1 mark]*. / In the eye wall there are very strong winds, torrential rain and a low temperature *[1 mark]*.

2.1 This question is level marked. How to grade your answer:
Level 0: There is no relevant information. *[0 marks]*
Level 1: There is a basic suggestion of how and why the distribution of tropical storms may change. *[1-2 marks]*
Level 2: There is a clear explanation of how and why the distribution of tropical storms may change. *[3-4 marks]*
Here are some points your answer may include:
- Tropical storms only form in areas where the sea temperature is 27 °C or higher.
- The graph shows an average global temperature increase of 0.5 °C over 50 years. This may have caused ocean temperatures to increase.
- If the warming continues, larger areas of ocean will be 27 °C or warmer.
- This means the area affected by tropical storms will increase in size, with areas at higher latitudes affected.

CGP

GCSE AQA Geography

For the Grade 9-1 Course

Exam Practice Answer Book

Contents

Unit 1: Living with the Physical Environment

Unit 2: Challenges in the Human Environment

Unit 3: Geographical Applications

Published by CGP

ISBN: 978 1 78294 612 0

www.cgpbooks.co.uk
Printed by Elanders Ltd, Newcastle upon Tyne
Clipart from Corel®

Graph on page 16 from Annual Urban Population at Mid-Year, by UN Population Division, © 2016 United Nations.
Reprinted with the permission of the United Nations. https://esa.un.org/unpd/wup/DataQuery/

Based on the classic CGP style created by Richard Parsons.

Unit 1: Living with the Physical Environment

Pages 11-12: Tropical Storms — Effects and Responses

1.1   Any two from: e.g. buildings were destroyed *[1 mark]* / roads were damaged *[1 mark]* / electricity supplies were damaged *[1 mark]*.

You won't get any marks for giving primary effects that cannot be seen in Figure 1.

1.2   Any two from: e.g. evacuate people before the storm arrives *[1 mark]*. / Rescue people who have been cut off by flooding *[1 mark]*. / Treat injured people *[1 mark]*. / Set up temporary shelters for people whose homes have been flooded or damaged *[1 mark]*. / Provide temporary supplies of water, food, electricity, gas and communications systems *[1 mark]*.

1.3   Any two from: e.g. repair homes or rehouse people who have been displaced due to damaged buildings *[1 mark]*. / Repair or replace damaged infrastructure *[1 mark]*. / Repair and improve flood defence systems, e.g. levees and floodgates *[1 mark]*. / Improve forecasting techniques to give people more warning in the future *[1 mark]*. / Provide aid, grants or subsidies to repair and strengthen homes *[1 mark]*.

2.1   Predicting where and when a tropical storm will hit gives people in Miami time to evacuate, so fewer people will be injured or killed *[1 mark]*. It also gives people time to protect their homes and businesses, e.g. by boarding up windows, so there will be less damage to property *[1 mark]*

2.2   This question is level marked. How to grade your answer:

Level 0:   There is no relevant information. *[0 marks]*

Level 1:   There is a basic suggestion of how protection strategies can reduce the effects of tropical storms. *[1-2 marks]*

Level 2:   There is a clear explanation of how protection strategies can reduce the effects of tropical storms. *[3-4 marks]*

Here are some points your answer may include:

- Buildings can be designed to withstand tropical storms, e.g. by using reinforced concrete, to reduce damage and prevent deaths and injuries from debris.
- Buildings can also be put on stilts so they are safe from floodwater, reducing floodwater damage and allowing people to return home more quickly after a tropical storm.
- Flood defences can be built along rivers (e.g. levees) and coasts (e.g. sea walls) to prevent or reduce flooding so that fewer buildings are damaged.

2.3   This question is level marked. How to grade your answer:

Level 0:   There is no relevant information. *[0 marks]*

Level 1:   There is a basic explanation of how immediate and/or long-term responses reduced the effects of a named tropical storm. *[1-2 marks]*

Level 2:   There is a clear explanation of how immediate and/or long-term responses reduced the effects of a named tropical storm. *[3-4 marks]*

Level 3:   There is a detailed explanation of how immediate and/or long-term responses reduced the effects of a named tropical storm. *[5-6 marks]*

Your answer must refer to a named example.

Here are some points your answer may include:

- The immediate responses to the event, e.g. evacuation before the hurricane reached land; setting up control centres and emergency shelters; stockpiling supplies; the coastguard, police, fire service and army rescuing people; charities providing aid.
- How the immediate responses helped to reduce the effects of the storm, e.g. rescuing people from affected areas prevented deaths.
- The long-term responses to the event, e.g. government funds to rebuild homes and repair other essential infrastructure; not rebuilding on high risk areas; placing new buildings on stilts in high risk areas; repairing and improving flood defences.
- How the long-term responses helped to reduce the effects of the storm, e.g. aid to rebuild houses meant that people were not left homeless.
- Answers may refer to tropical storm events such as Typhoon Haiyan, which struck the Philippines in 2013. Warnings from the meteorological agency led to the evacuation of 800 000 people before the storm arrived; without these warnings, the death toll of 8000 may have been much higher. The UN appealed for over $300 million to rebuild homes and provide other relief after the storm, which helped the country recover.

Page 13: UK Weather Hazards

1.1   Any two from: e.g. lightning can cause death if it strikes a person *[1 mark]*. / Lightning can cause fires that damage property or the environment *[1 mark]*. / Thunderstorms can cause flooding due to torrential rain *[1 mark]*. / Thunderstorms can cause power cuts *[1 mark]*.

1.2   Any two from: e.g. people can experience health problems such as heat exhaustion *[1 mark]*. / Transport can be disrupted from rails buckling or roads melting *[1 mark]*. / Disruption to transport can delay people or goods, which can cause companies to incur more costs *[1 mark]*. / The tourism industry may benefit from people spending money on holidays and leisure in warm weather *[1 mark]*.

1.3   This question is level marked. How to grade your answer:

Level 0:   There is no relevant information. *[0 marks]*

Level 1:   There is a basic description of the evidence for the UK's weather becoming more extreme. *[1-2 marks]*

Level 2:   There is a clear description of the evidence for the UK's weather becoming more extreme. *[3-4 marks]*

Here are some points your answer may include:

- Temperatures have been extreme — the UK's ten warmest years on record have all occurred since 1990, and seven of the eleven coldest years have occurred since 1980.
- It's raining more — more rainfall records were broken in 2010-2014 than in any decade on record, even after only half a decade. December 2015 was the wettest month ever recorded in the UK.
- Major flooding occurs often — e.g. there was major flooding caused by storms and high rainfall in the Somerset Levels during the winter of 2013-2014, in west Wales in 2012 and in Cumbria in 2005, 2009 and 2015-2016 (along with large parts of northern England and parts of Scotland).

1.4   This question is level marked. There are also 3 extra marks available for spelling, punctuation and grammar. How to grade your answer:

Level 0:   There is no relevant information. *[0 marks]*

Level 1:   There is a basic description of the social and economic effects caused by an extreme weather event in the UK. *[1-3 marks]*

Level 2:   There is a clear comparison of the social and economic effects caused by an extreme weather event in the UK and a conclusion. *[4-6 marks]*

Level 3:   There is a detailed comparison of the social and economic effects caused by an extreme weather event in the UK and a clear conclusion. *[7-9 marks]*

Make sure your spelling, punctuation and grammar is consistently correct, that your meaning is clear and that you use a range of geographical terms correctly *[0-3 marks]*.

Your answer must evaluate the relative significance of a specific extreme weather event in the UK. You have to decide whether the economic effects were more or less significant than the social effects and explain your decision.

Unit 1: Living with the Physical Environment

Here are some points your answer may include:
- The economic effects of the event, e.g. increased costs or reduced productivity for businesses due to disruption to transport networks, including flooded roads; people being unable to get to work; sales being reduced because customers couldn't get to shops; loss of tourism in the affected area; the cost of repairing any damage.
- The social effects of the events, e.g. homes being flooded and people forced to evacuate; settlements being cut off; people being unable to insure their homes against future events; schools closing.
- Answers may refer to the Somerset Levels flooding in the winter of 2013-2014, which flooded more than 600 homes and left some villages completely inaccessible by road. The total cost of damage was over £80 million and local companies lost more than £1.2 million of business.

Unit 1A — Climate Change

Pages 14-15 — Climate Change — Evidence and Causes

1.1 Temperature has changed in cycles of approximately 100 000 years *[1 mark]*. The temperature difference ranges between -9°C and +3°C from the present day *[1 mark]*.

1.2 Ice sheets are made up of layers of ice, with one new layer formed each year *[1 mark]*. By analysing the gases trapped in the layers of ice, scientists can tell what the temperature was in each year *[1 mark]*.

1.3 Any two from: e.g. cores from trees contain rings that can be counted to find the age of a tree *[1 mark]*. The thickness of each ring shows what the climate was like *[1 mark]*. / Pollen from plants that has been preserved in sediment, e.g. at the bottom of lakes or in peat bogs, can be identified and dated to show which species were living at that time *[1 mark]*. This can be compared to the conditions that similar species live in now, to identify what the climate was like at the time *[1 mark]*. / The remains of organisms found in cores taken from ocean sediments can be analysed *[1 mark]*. Scientists can use their knowledge of the conditions that the organisms need to survive to determine what the climate was like at the time *[1 mark]*.

1.4 Any two from: the path of the Earth's orbit around the Sun changes from an almost perfect circle to an ellipse *[1 mark]*. This affects the amount of solar radiation/energy that the Earth receives. If the Earth receives more energy, it gets warmer *[1 mark]*. / The Sun's output of energy changes in short cycles of about 11 years *[1 mark]*. Periods when solar output is reduced may cause the Earth's climate to become cooler in some areas *[1 mark]*. / Major volcanic eruptions eject large quantities of material into the atmosphere *[1 mark]*. Some of these particles reflect the Sun's rays back out to space, so the Earth's surface cools *[1 mark]*.

2.1 0.85 °C (accept 0.8-0.9 °C) *[1 mark]*

2.2 The temperature stayed between about 13.5 and 13.8 °C between 1860 and 1930 *[1 mark]*, and then rose fairly steadily to around 14.4 °C by 2000 *[1 mark]*.

3.1 This question is level marked. How to grade your answer:
   Level 0: There is no relevant information. *[0 marks]*
   Level 1: There is a basic explanation of the impact of coal-fired power plants on climate change. *[1-2 marks]*
   Level 2: There is a clear explanation of the impact of coal-fired power plants on climate change. *[3-4 marks]*
   Here are some points your answer may include:
   - Burning coal, a fossil fuel, is likely to increase global warming.
   - Carbon dioxide is released into the atmosphere when coal is burnt as fuel.
   - Coal-fired power plants therefore increase the concentration of greenhouse gases in the atmosphere.
   - Greenhouse gases absorb outgoing heat, so less is lost to space.
   - Increasing the amount of greenhouse gas in the atmosphere means more heat is trapped and the planet warms up.

3.2 Any two from: e.g. deforestation reduces the number of trees, so less carbon dioxide is removed from the atmosphere *[1 mark]*. / If trees are burnt, carbon dioxide is released into the atmosphere *[1 mark]*. / Farming of livestock produces a lot of methane, which is a greenhouse gas *[1 mark]*. / Growing rice can contribute to global warming, because flooded fields emit methane (a greenhouse gas) *[1 mark]*. / Producing cement releases CO_2 (a greenhouse gas) because cement is made from limestone, which contains carbon *[1 mark]*.

Page 16 — Effects of Climate Change

1.1 30 cm (accept 29 or 31 cm) *[1 mark]*

1.2 Any one from: e.g. low-lying and coastal areas may be flooded more regularly *[1 mark]*. / Coastal erosion may increase with sea level rise *[1 mark]*. / Some coastal areas might be submerged, so habitats might be lost *[1 mark]*.

1.3 Any two from: e.g. warmer temperatures may cause glaciers to shrink and ice sheets like Greenland to melt, leading to the loss of polar habitats *[1 mark]*. / Some species that are adapted to particular climates may decline if they don't adapt to the changing climate *[1 mark]*. / Precipitation patterns may change, affecting how much rain areas get *[1 mark]*. / The distribution of some species could change and biodiversity could decrease *[1 mark]*.

2.1 The overall decrease in rainfall from 1995 to 2015 corresponds to a decrease in maize yield *[1 mark]*. This suggests that climate change may be causing crop yields to decrease *[1 mark]*.

2.2 Any one from: e.g. farmers' incomes may decrease if it becomes too dry for farming *[1 mark]*. / Less food being grown could lead to malnutrition, ill health and death from starvation *[1 mark]*.

2.3 Any one from: e.g. in some places deaths due to heat may increase, but deaths due to cold may decrease *[1 mark]*. / Some areas could become so hot and dry that they're difficult or impossible to inhabit so people are forced to move *[1 mark]*. / Low-lying coastal areas could be lost to the sea or flood so often that they become impossible to inhabit, so people have to move *[1 mark]*. / Migration due to changing environmental conditions may cause overcrowding in other areas *[1 mark]*. / Some areas may struggle to supply enough water for their residents due to problems with water availability caused by changing rainfall patterns *[1 mark]*. / Problems with water availability may lead to political tensions, especially where rivers cross borders *[1 mark]*. / Climate change may make the weather more extreme, so more money may need to be spent on predicting extreme weather events, reducing their impacts and rebuilding after them *[1 mark]*.

Page 17 — Managing Climate Change

1.1 Building houses on stilts means that people can continue to live in areas that are flooded by rising sea levels *[1 mark]*. This means that people can remain safe and don't lose their homes or possessions *[1 mark]*.
You won't get any marks for writing about responses that cannot be seen in Figure 1.

1.2 Any one from: e.g. physical defences such as flood barriers could be built to cope with rising sea levels *[1 mark]*. / Better flood warning systems could be put in place to cope with rising sea levels *[1 mark]*.

Answers

Unit 1: Living with the Physical Environment

2.1   This question is level marked. How to grade your answer:
Level 0:   There is no relevant information. *[0 marks]*
Level 1:   There is a basic description of at least one way that greenhouse gas emissions could be reduced. *[1-2 marks]*
Level 2:   There is a clear explanation of several ways that greenhouse gas emissions could be reduced. *[3-4 marks]*
Here are some points your answer may include:
- Replacing fossil fuels with nuclear power and renewable energy can help reduce greenhouse gas emissions from power stations.
- More offshore wind farms could be built, as is happening in East Anglia; wave and tidal power projects could be introduced; new nuclear power plants could be built.
- Carbon Capture and Storage (CCS) is a new technology designed to reduce emissions from fossil fuel burning power stations. CCS involves capturing CO_2 and transporting it to places where it can be stored safely, e.g. deep underground.

2.2   International agreements mean that many countries around the world work together to try to reduce emissions, so that the concentration of greenhouse gases in the atmosphere doesn't increase too much, reducing the possible impacts of climate change *[1 mark]*. Some international agreements, such as the Paris Agreement, require countries to cut emissions by a certain amount, so countries have to think about where their emissions are coming from and make changes to reduce them *[1 mark]*.

Unit 1B — Ecosystems

Page 18: Ecosystems

1.1   D *[1 mark]*
A producer is an organism that uses energy from sunlight to produce food, so producers are usually plants rather than animals.

1.2   Any one from: sea urchin *[1 mark]* / sea otter *[1 mark]* / octopus *[1 mark]* / sea snail *[1 mark]* / crab *[1 mark]* / periwinkle *[1 mark]*

1.3   **Octopuses:** The population will decrease because there will be fewer crabs for them to eat *[1 mark]*.
Seaweed: The population of seaweed will increase because less of it will be being eaten by the crabs *[1 mark]*.

1.4   A bigger population of sea otters would cause the populations of octopuses, crabs and sea urchins to fall because more of them would be being eaten *[1 mark]*. This would cause the population of sea snails to increase because there would be fewer octopuses feeding on them *[1 mark]*. The population of seaweed would increase because there would be fewer sea urchins and crabs feeding on it *[1 mark]*.

1.5   This question is level marked. How to grade your answer:
Level 0:   There is no relevant information. *[0 marks]*
Level 1:   There is a basic description of some parts of the nutrient cycle. *[1-2 marks]*
Level 2:   There is a clear explanation of the complete nutrient cycle. *[3-4 marks]*
Here are some points your answer may include:
- When dead material decomposes, nutrients are released into the soil.
- The nutrients are then taken up from the soil by plants.
- The plants may be eaten by consumers, so the nutrients they contain are transferred to the consumers.
- When the plants or consumers die, the nutrients are returned to the soil, and the cycle continues.

Page 19: Global Ecosystems

1.1   Tropical rainforests are found around the equator *[1 mark]*, in areas such as central America / northeast South America / central Africa / south east Asia *[1 mark]*.

1.2   Hot deserts are found between approximately 15° and 30° north and south of the equator *[1 mark]*, in areas such as north Africa / southwest USA / Australia *[1 mark]*.

1.3   B *[1 mark]*
Deciduous forests are found mainly in the mid latitudes, where there are four distinct seasons. Summers are warm and winters are colder. Deciduous trees lose their leaves in winter to cope with the colder weather.

1.4   Tundra is found at **high** *[1 mark]* latitudes, including areas such as **northern Canada** *[1 mark]* / **northern Russia** *[1 mark]* / **the coast of Greenland** *[1 mark]* / **northern Europe** *[1 mark]*. The **cold** *[1 mark]* winters, and **low** *[1 mark]* rainfall mean that vegetation is sparse.

Unit 1B — Tropical Rainforests

Page 20: Tropical Rainforests

1.1   E.g. many trees are very tall *[1 mark]*. / The vegetation cover is dense *[1 mark]*. / Most trees are evergreen *[1 mark]*.

1.2   E.g. many animals rely on plants for food *[1 mark]*. The dense, varied vegetation provides lots of food, so it can support high animal populations *[1 mark]*.

1.3   The climate is the same all year round / there are no definite seasons *[1 mark]*. It's hot (the temperature is generally between 20-28 °C and only varies by a few degrees over the year) *[1 mark]*. Rainfall is very high (around 2000 mm per year) and it rains every day *[1 mark]*.

1.4   Fallen leaves decay quickly in the hot, moist climate, so there is a nutrient-rich surface layer of soil *[1 mark]*. Heavy rain washes nutrients away, so the lower levels of soil aren't very fertile *[1 mark]*.

1.5   The nutrient-rich surface layer of soil means that plants can grow quickly and vegetation is dense *[1 mark]*. Plants lose leaves all year round, returning nutrients to the soil, so the top layer of the soil remains fertile *[1 mark]*.

Page 21: Tropical Rainforests — Biodiversity

1.1   **A:** There is lots of light but it is exposed to wind and heavy rainfall *[1 mark]*.
B: It is sheltered and quite dark because of the trees above *[1 mark]*.

1.2   Any two from: e.g. the trees are very tall so that they can break through the canopy layer to reach the sunlight *[1 mark]*. / The trees have big buttress roots to support their trunks *[1 mark]*. / They only have leaves at their crown, where there's most light *[1 mark]*.

1.3   Any one from: e.g. plants have thick, waxy leaves so that water easily runs off *[1 mark]*. / Leaves often have pointed drip tips to channel the water off *[1 mark]*. / Many trees have smooth, thin bark to allow water to run off easily *[1 mark]*. / Plants drop their leaves gradually throughout the year, meaning they can go on growing all year round *[1 mark]*. / Climbing plants, such as lianas, use the tree trunks to climb up to the sunlight *[1 mark]*.

1.4   **B:** Any one from: e.g. animals such as anteaters have a sharp sense of smell and hearing, so they can detect predators on the dark forest floor *[1 mark]*. / Some animals have striped or spotted coats to camouflage them in the dappled light *[1 mark]*.
C: Any one from: e.g. animals such as howler monkeys have strong limbs to help them climb and leap from tree to tree *[1 mark]*. / Some animals have flaps of skin that enable them to glide between trees, e.g. flying squirrels *[1 mark]*. They may have suction cups for climbing, e.g. red-eyed tree frogs *[1 mark]*. / Birds such as harpy eagles have short, pointy wings so that they can easily manoeuvre between the dense tangle of branches in the trees *[1 mark]*.

Unit 1: Living with the Physical Environment

1.5 E.g. development tends to destroy habitats, which can reduce biodiversity *[1 mark]*. This is because many species only live in a particular habitat, so if that habitat is destroyed, the species can be made extinct *[1 mark]*. Many organisms are dependent on other species in the ecosystem, so if one species is made extinct it will affect other species *[1 mark]*.

Page 22: Tropical Rainforests — Deforestation

1.1 The area of deforested land increased between 1966 and 2016 *[1 mark]*. The rate of deforestation was slow at first, but increased rapidly after 1996 *[1 mark]*.

1.2 Any two from: e.g. as the population in the area increases, trees are cleared to make land for new settlements *[1 mark]*. / Some areas have deposits, e.g. of gold or iron ore, so trees are cleared to make space for mines *[1 mark]*. / Building dams to generate hydro-electric power floods large areas of forest *[1 mark]*. / Trees are felled to be sold as timber *[1 mark]*. / Road building for logging requires tree clearance *[1 mark]*. / The forest may be cleared for commercial farming, such as cattle grazing, palm oil or soya plantations *[1 mark]*. / The forest may be cleared for subsistence farming so farmers can grow food for themselves and their families *[1 mark]*.

1.3 Any one from: e.g. logging, mining and farming create jobs *[1 mark]*. / A lot of money is made from selling timber, extracted minerals and animals/crops *[1 mark]*.

1.4 Any two from: e.g. with no trees to hold the soil together, heavy rain washes away the soil *[1 mark]*. Soil entering rivers can reduce their capacity, leading to flooding *[1 mark]*. / Without a tree canopy to intercept rainfall and tree roots to absorb it, more water reaches the soil *[1 mark]*. This reduces soil fertility as nutrients in the soil are washed away, out of reach of plants *[1 mark]*. / Trees remove CO_2 from the atmosphere, and burning vegetation to clear the forest produces CO_2 *[1 mark]*. So deforestation means more CO_2 in the atmosphere, which adds to the greenhouse effect *[1 mark]*.

1.5 This question is level marked. There are 3 extra marks available for spelling, punctuation and grammar.
How to grade your answer:
Level 0: There is no relevant information. *[0 marks]*
Level 1: There is a basic description of some of the benefits of deforestation to the people that live in the rainforest. *[1-3 marks]*
Level 2: There is a clear description of some of the benefits of deforestation to the people that live in the rainforest and some reference to the problems that it may cause. *[4-6 marks]*
Level 3: There is a detailed description of some of the benefits of deforestation to the people that live in the rainforest and a clear analysis of the problems that it may cause. The answer comes to a clear conclusion. *[7-9 marks]*
Make sure your spelling, punctuation and grammar is consistently correct, that your meaning is clear and that you use a range of geographical terms correctly *[0-3 marks]*.
Your answer must refer to a named example.
Here are some points your answer may include:
• Deforestation brings benefits to people who live in the rainforest, e.g. it clears land for subsistence farming, so people can feed their families; industries such as logging and mining create jobs; road building improves access.
• Deforestation brings wealth to countries (e.g. through exporting hardwood, minerals etc. from the rainforest). This may have knock-on benefits for the people living in the area, such as investment in providing education or electricity to the area.
• However, deforestation also brings problems for the people living in rainforests. For example, local rubber tappers who extract natural rubber from rubber trees may lose their livelihoods as trees are cut down.

• Subsistence and commercial farmers may find that their land soon becomes unproductive, and they are forced to move or clear more land. This is because removing tree cover removes the means by which soil nutrients are replenished, and leaves the soil exposed to erosion by heavy rainfall, so it quickly becomes infertile.
• Your answer may refer to deforestation in the Amazon rainforest, for reasons such as energy development and commercial farming in Brazil and the construction of the Trans-Amazonian Highway.

The question asks you to 'assess the extent'. This means you need to weigh up the pros and cons of the deforestation of tropical rainforests for the people who live there, and come to a clear conclusion about whether the benefits outweigh the problems.

Pages 23-24: Tropical Rainforests — Sustainable Management

1.1 New trees can be planted to replace the ones that are cut down *[1 mark]*. This preserves tree cover so there will be trees for people to use in the future *[1 mark]*.

1.2 Activities such as logging are restricted in National Parks, so deforestation is reduced *[1 mark]*.

1.3 International agreements try to reduce illegal logging, which prevents large areas of land being deforested unsustainably *[1 mark]*. They also encourage consumers to buy hardwood from sustainably managed rainforests *[1 mark]*, which makes sustainable management of rainforests more profitable, encouraging countries to manage rainforests in this way *[1 mark]*.

1.4 Only some trees are felled — most trees are left standing, so the forest structure is less damaged *[1 mark]*. The canopy is still there and the soil isn't exposed, so the soil remains fertile and is able to support plant growth *[1 mark]*. This means that the forest will be able to regenerate so it can be used in the future *[1 mark]*.

1.5 The country may be allowing logging, farming and mining in its rainforests to make money to pay its debt *[1 mark]*. Reducing the debt would mean the country wouldn't have to do this, so the rainforest would be conserved for the future *[1 mark]*.

2.1 2250 tourists *[1 mark]*

2.2

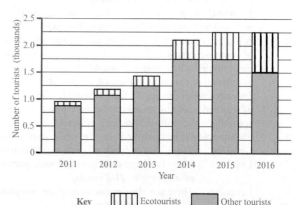

[1 mark]

2.3 The number of ecotourists has increased *[1 mark]* from about 100 in 2011 to 750 in 2016 *[1 mark]*.

2.4 E.g. people may be more aware of the threats to tropical rainforests and the need to conserve them *[1 mark]*. They may want to decrease their own impact on the rainforest, so they choose to travel as ecotourists *[1 mark]*.

2.5 This question is level marked. How to grade your answer:
Level 0: There is no relevant information. *[0 marks]*
Level 1: There is a basic explanation of how ecotourism helps in the sustainable management of tropical rainforests. *[1-2 marks]*
Level 2: There is a clear explanation of how ecotourism helps in the sustainable management of tropical rainforests. *[3-4 marks]*

Unit 1: Living with the Physical Environment

Here are some points your answer may include:
- Ecotourism minimises environmental impacts, e.g. by making sure waste and litter are disposed of properly to prevent land and water contamination. This helps to make sure that the tropical rainforest isn't damaged.
- Ecotourism provides a source of income for local people, e.g. they act as guides, and provide accommodation and transport. If local people are employed in tourism, they don't have to log or farm to make money, meaning fewer trees are cut down.
- Ecotourism can bring in more money for rainforest conservation. This money can be used to e.g. monitor conservation areas to make sure that restrictions on damaging activities are kept to.
- If a country's economy relies on ecotourism, there's an incentive to conserve the environment. This means that it is more likely to be protected for the future.

2.6   Any one from: e.g. some local people may not know what the environmental impacts of deforestation are so they may try to make money (e.g. by illegal logging) *[1 mark]*. Educating local people about the impacts of deforestation and ways to reduce the impacts means they may use the rainforest in a less damaging, more sustainable way *[1 mark]*. / Some local people may not be aware of ways to make a living without damaging the rainforest *[1 mark]*. Educating local people about alternative ways to make money, e.g. ecotourism, means they aren't dependent on unsustainable options in order to make a living *[1 mark]*.

Unit 1B — Hot Deserts

Pages 25-26: Hot Deserts
1.1   40 °C *[1 mark]*
1.2   Any two from: e.g. temperature shows a high daily variation, being very hot in the day and much colder at night *[1 mark]*, e.g. Figure 1 shows that the difference between maximum and minimum temperature in January is about 20 °C *[1 mark]*. / There is very little rainfall *[1 mark]*, e.g. Figure 1 shows that the average rainfall peaks at about 25 mm a month but can be as low as about 5 mm a month *[1 mark]*. / There is a lot of sunshine all year round *[1 mark]*, e.g. there is an average of at least 7 hours of sunshine every day *[1 mark]*.
2.1   E.g. low rainfall means that soils are dry *[1 mark]*, while high temperatures mean that evaporation rates are high so soils are dry and salty *[1 mark]*. Dry soils are easily eroded and can form dust clouds, which inhibit rainfall *[1 mark]*.
2.2   Any two from: e.g. extracting groundwater by digging wells means people are able to grow more crops in the short-term, so human populations in the area may increase *[1 mark]*. / In the long-term, extracting water reduces soil moisture, leaving soil drier and more easily eroded *[1 mark]*. / Drier soil means that plants will die, so vegetation cover decreases *[1 mark]*.
3.1   Any three from: e.g. plant roots are extremely long to reach very deep water supplies *[1 mark]*. / Plant roots spread out very wide near the surface to catch as much water as possible when it rains *[1 mark]*. / Cacti have thick waxy skin to reduce water loss *[1 mark]*. / Plants have spines or small spiky leaves to reduce water loss *[1 mark]*. / Cacti have swollen stems to store water *[1 mark]*.
4.1   Any two from: e.g. large ears give a large surface area, which helps the jerboa to lose heat *[1 mark]*. / Large feet help the jerboa move without sinking into the sand *[1 mark]*. / Jerboas are nocturnal, so they can avoid the heat in the daytime and save energy *[1 mark]*. / Jerboas live in underground burrows, where temperatures are lower *[1 mark]*.
5.1   Biodiversity is highest around water sources, such as the oasis shown in Figure 5 *[1 mark]*.

5.2   This question is level marked. How to grade your answer:
Level 0:   There is no relevant information. *[0 marks]*
Level 1:   There is a basic explanation of why biodiversity in hot desert environments is vulnerable to human activity. *[1-2 marks]*
Level 2:   There is a clear explanation of why biodiversity in hot desert environments is vulnerable to human activity. *[3-4 marks]*
Here are some points your answer may include:
- Hot deserts have relatively low biodiversity and contain a high proportion of species that are endemic (unique to that location).
- Most species of plants and animals live near water sources, and this is also where human populations are highest. Human activity in these areas is therefore likely to have a negative effect on biodiversity.
- If water sources are used up (e.g. for irrigation) or contaminated (e.g. by livestock), there is no water available for plants and animals, so they may die.
- Human activities are thought to be contributing to climate change. Climate change may make some desert environments hotter and drier, so species that are adapted to particular conditions may move or die out.

Page 27: Development in Hot Deserts
1.1   E.g. economic opportunities at Location A may include mining and commercial farming *[1 mark]*. There are mineral resources to the north of the town, which could encourage mining companies to extract them for export *[1 mark]*. The town is also situated on the river, so there is water for irrigation, so there are opportunities for commercial farming, e.g. to the south of the town *[1 mark]*.
You may also have chosen to write about opportunities for tourism, so you would still get a mark for writing something like 'The town is quite large and has road links to the wildlife reserve to the west, so it may appeal to tourists.'
1.2   E.g. there are no roads near to Location C, so it is inaccessible *[1 mark]*. This would make it difficult for tourists or workers to reach the area *[1 mark]*. / Location C is a long way from the river and relies on a borehole for water *[1 mark]*. This would make it difficult to develop the area, because most development (e.g. for industry, farming or tourists) require a large, reliable supply of water *[1 mark]*.
1.3   This question is level marked. How to grade your answer:
Level 0:   There is no relevant information. *[0 marks]*
Level 1:   There is a basic description of the extent of settlement at Location B and Location D. *[1-2 marks]*
Level 2:   There is a clear description of the extent of settlement at the two locations, with several reasons for this pattern. *[3-4 marks]*
Level 3:   There is a detailed description of the extent of settlement at the two locations and a clear explanation of multiple possible reasons for this pattern. *[5-6 marks]*
Here are some points your answer may include:
- Location B has been quite extensively developed.
- Oil reserves at the site give the opportunity for their exploration and extraction. This creates jobs and means that people move to the area and settle there, creating more opportunities for e.g. retail and service industries.
- The town is connected by road and the river provides a water supply, allowing the industries to develop.
- In contrast, development at Location D is limited to subsistence farming.
- A water source provides sufficient water for small-scale farming, but there is not enough water for large-scale farming or other industries to develop.
- There are no roads close to Location D, so the area is also inaccessible, hindering development of tourism.

Unit 1: Living with the Physical Environment

1.4   This question is level marked. There are also 3 extra marks available for spelling, punctuation and grammar. How to grade your answer:

Level 0:   There is no relevant information. *[0 marks]*

Level 1:   There is a basic description of the opportunities and challenges for development in a named hot desert environment. *[1-3 marks]*

Level 2:   There is a clear description and explanation of opportunities and challenges for development in a named hot desert environment. *[4-6 marks]*

Level 3:   There is a detailed description and explanation of the opportunities and challenges for development in a named hot desert environment. *[7-9 marks]*

Make sure your spelling, punctuation and grammar is consistently correct, that your meaning is clear and that you use a range of geographical terms correctly *[0-3 marks]*.

Your answer must refer to a named example.

Here are some points your answer may include:
- Hot deserts may provide opportunities for development, including farming, mineral extraction, energy production and tourism.
- However, there are also challenges to development, for example extreme temperatures, inaccessibility and limited water supply.
- Development can also damage fragile hot desert environments, which can take a long time to recover.
- Answers may refer to development in the Sahara, which is the world's largest hot desert. It offers numerous opportunities for development, such as extraction of phosphate in Morocco, and the construction of the Aswan Dam, which boosts opportunities for farming in Egypt. Because of its challenges, such as daytime temperatures of over 40 °C and a lack of roads, the population of the Sahara is low and development is limited.

Page 28: Desertification

1.1   Desertification is the process of land becoming more like **a desert** *[1 mark]*. When soil is exposed, it is easily removed by **wind** *[1 mark]* and **water** *[1 mark]*.

1.2   This question is level marked. How to grade your answer:

Level 0:   There is no relevant information. *[0 marks]*

Level 1:   There is a basic description of at least one human cause of desertification. *[1-2 marks]*

Level 2:   There is a clear description of some of the ways that humans contribute to the process of desertification. *[3-4 marks]*

Level 3:   There is a detailed description of a number of ways that humans contribute to the process of desertification. *[5-6 marks]*

Here are some points your answer may include:
- People living in the area may have removed vegetation for firewood. Removal of trees leaves the soil exposed so it is more easily eroded.
- Keeping too many animals in a small area can cause overgrazing of vegetation, whilst trampling can contribute to erosion.
- Overcultivation of the land can mean that nutrients are used up. This means that plants can no longer be grown in those soils, and without plants, soil erosion increases because their roots no longer hold the soil together.
- Population growth puts pressure on the land, leading to more deforestation (for firewood), more over-grazing and more over-cultivation.
- Human activities are also contributing to climate change.
- Climate change is expected to reduce rainfall in areas that are already quite dry. Less rain means that less water is available for plant growth, so plants begin to die. Plant roots hold the soil together. If the plants die, the soil is easily eroded.

- Climate change is expected to increase global temperature. Higher temperatures would mean that more water would evaporate from the land and from plants. This would make soils drier and mean that plants would die (so their roots would no longer hold the soil together).

2.1   Drip irrigation is more efficient *[1 mark]* because it uses 2.5 million litres less per hectare than furrow irrigation every year *[1 mark]*.

2.2   E.g. adding a small amount of water more gradually means that soil is not eroded *[1 mark]*. When soil is eroded, nutrients are lost and plants can't grow, so eventually the ground becomes dry and dusty *[1 mark]*.

Unit 1B — Cold Environments

Page 29: Cold Environments — Polar and Tundra

1.1   July *[1 mark]*

1.2   The climate is cold all year around, e.g. the maximum average temperature is 9 °C in July and the minimum is –9 °C in January *[1 mark]*. Rainfall is generally low, e.g. it is only 57 mm in April *[1 mark]*.

2.1   The cold climate causes plants to decompose very slowly *[1 mark]*. This means that the soil is relatively low in nutrients *[1 mark]*.

2.2   E.g. damaging plant cover can cause permafrost to melt *[1 mark]*. Melting permafrost can release trapped greenhouse gases *[1 mark]*. These contribute to global warming, leading to changes in the climate of cold environments *[1 mark]*.

Page 30: Cold Environments — Biodiversity

1.1   Any one from: e.g. the Arctic fox has a light-coloured coat to camouflage it against the snow *[1 mark]* so it can sneak up on prey *[1 mark]*. / It has thick fur *[1 mark]* to reduce the amount of energy needed to keep warm *[1 mark]*.

1.2   E.g. it is low-growing and round-shaped to provide protection from the wind *[1 mark]*. It has small leaves to limit the amount of moisture lost through transpiration *[1 mark]*.

Make sure the adaptations that you write about are visible in the figure — the plant may by adapted in other ways, but if you can't see it in the photograph you won't get the marks for it.

1.3   B *[1 mark]*

1.4   E.g. warming may cause Arctic foxes to move towards the poles, where it is cooler *[1 mark]*. If warming leads to loss of the polar environment, or if the Arctic foxes can't move further towards the poles, they may be at risk of decline or extinction *[1 mark]*.

Page 31: Development in Cold Environments

1.1   Economic opportunities at location A include fishing and tourism *[1 mark]*. The town is on the coast with easy access to fishing areas *[1 mark]*. The nearby airport and roads make the town accessible to tourists, who may visit to go whale-watching *[1 mark]*.

1.2   E.g. the only access route to location B by land is a long, twisty ice road that may not be usable all year round *[1 mark]*. This could make it difficult for people to access the area, which could limit the development of e.g. tourism *[1 mark]*.

The question tells you to use evidence from the map, so make sure your answer refers to features you can see on the map.

1.3   This question is level marked. How to grade your answer:

Level 0:   There is no relevant information. *[0 marks]*

Level 1:   There is a basic description of the extent of settlement at the two locations, with some suggestion of a reason for the difference. *[1-2 marks]*

Level 2:   There is a clear description of the extent of settlement at the two locations, with several possible reasons for the difference. *[3-4 marks]*

Unit 1: Living with the Physical Environment

Here are some points your answer may include:
- Location D is a much larger settlement than location C, suggesting that more people live there.
- Oil extraction is the main industry at location D, and the large number of oil wells suggests that there are extensive reserves there. This would create lots of jobs, which would attract people to the area.
- Mining is the main industry at location C, but the mineral reserves appear to be less extensive than the oil reserves at location D, so it probably provides fewer jobs.
- Location D is more accessible than location C. It is situated on the main road and is close to the airport. This would make it easier for industry to develop there, providing jobs and attracting more people.
- In contrast, location C is situated in a hilly region, far from the airport and with only a steep minor road serving it. This would make it hard for industry to develop, so there may be fewer jobs, and therefore fewer people settling there.

1.4 This question is level marked. There are 3 extra marks available for spelling, punctuation and grammar.
How to grade your answer:
Level 0: There is no relevant information. *[0 marks]*
Level 1: There is a basic description of the opportunities and challenges for development in a named cold environment. *[1-3 marks]*
Level 2: There is a clear description and some explanation of the opportunities and challenges for development in a named cold environment. *[4-6 marks]*
Level 3: There is a detailed description and explanation of the opportunities and challenges for development in a named cold environment. *[7-9 marks]*
Make sure your spelling, punctuation and grammar is consistently correct, that your meaning is clear and that you use a range of geographical terms correctly *[0-3 marks]*.
Your answer must refer to a named example.
Here are some points your answer may include:
- Cold environments may include opportunities for development, for example oil and gas extraction, mineral resource mining, fishing and tourism.
- There are also significant challenges to development, for example extreme temperatures, inaccessibility and the difficulty of constructing permanent buildings and infrastructure.
- Development such as oil extraction and mineral mining can damage fragile cold environments, which can take a very long time to recover.
- Answers may refer to development in Alaska, where oil and gas extraction makes up over half the state's income but where the main oil field, around Prudhoe Bay, is very inaccessible and very cold with a mean annual temperature of –9 °C. The trans-Alaska oil pipeline had to be built across the tundra due to the inaccessibility of Prudhoe Bay to large shipping.

Page 32: Cold Environments — Sustainable Management

1.1 Any two from: e.g. it provides habitats for organisms, so it helps to protect biodiversity *[1 mark]*. / It gives scientists the opportunity to study wild plants and animals in their natural habitats *[1 mark]*. / Studying natural ecosystems can help scientists to replicate these conditions to help conserve rare species in managed environments *[1 mark]*. / If it is damaged it will take a long time to recover *[1 mark]*.

1.2 Any one from: e.g. the mining operation could cause ground and water pollution *[1 mark]*. / Heated buildings can warm the ground, causing permafrost to melt so that the ground becomes boggy *[1 mark]*. / Habitats could have been destroyed to make way for the mine *[1 mark]*. / Removal of vegetation could lead to melting of the permafrost layer (as plants would no longer be there to absorb heat from the sun) *[1 mark]*.

1.3 This question is level marked. How to grade your answer:
Level 0: There is no relevant information. *[0 marks]*
Level 1: There is a basic description of the need for development and the need for conservation in cold environments. *[1-2 marks]*
Level 2: There is a clear description of the need for development and the need for conservation in cold environments, and a basic conclusion regarding the extent to which these can be balanced. *[3-4 marks]*
Level 3: There is a detailed description of the need for development and the need for conservation in cold environments, and a clear conclusion regarding the extent to which these can be balanced. *[5-6 marks]*
You must decide to what extent the need for development and the need for conservation can be balanced, and explain your decision.
Here are some points your answer may include:
- People living in cold environments need to be able to exploit economic opportunities to provide jobs and earn money, e.g. from mining, tourism and mineral extraction. However, cold environments are fragile and often pristine natural ecosystems that are worth conserving and can take a long time to recover.
- Governments can introduce laws (e.g. the 1964 Wilderness Act in the USA) to protect parts of cold environments from development and regulate potentially damaging economic activities.
- International agreements can be made between countries to protect uninhabited areas, for example the 1959 Antarctic Treaty limits visitors to Antarctica and prohibits nuclear activities.
- Conservation groups, e.g. the World Wildlife Fund and Greenpeace, can pressure governments into taking action to protect cold environments that are at risk or have been damaged.
- Technology can be used to prevent or minimise environmental problems caused by development, for example using modern construction methods like elevating buildings on piles or building on gravel beds can prevent buildings warming the ground and melting the permafrost.

Unit 1C — Coastal Landscapes in the UK

Page 33 — Coastal Weathering and Erosion

1.1 The coast retreated between 2005 and 2015, particularly near Millom del Sol *[1 mark]*. The wave-cut platform near Millom del Sol became much wider as the cliff retreated *[1 mark]*.

1.2 Any two from: hydraulic power *[1 mark]* is when waves crash against rock and compress the air in the cracks. This puts pressure on the rock. Repeated compression widens the cracks and makes bits of rock break off *[1 mark]*. / Abrasion *[1 mark]* is when eroded particles in the water scrape and rub against rock, removing small pieces *[1 mark]*. / Attrition *[1 mark]* is when eroded particles in the water smash into each other and break into smaller fragments *[1 mark]*.

1.3 This question is level marked. How to grade your answer:
Level 0: There is no relevant information. *[0 marks]*
Level 1: There is a basic description of how freeze-thaw weathering causes cliffs to break up. *[1-2 marks]*
Level 2: There is a clear description of how freeze-thaw weathering causes cliffs to break up. *[3-4 marks]*

Unit 1: Living with the Physical Environment

Here are some points your answer may include:
- Freeze-thaw weathering can happen when water gets into rock that has cracks.
- If the water freezes it expands, which puts pressure on the rock.
- When the water thaws it contracts, which releases the pressure on the rock.
- Repeated freezing and thawing widens the cracks and causes the rock to break up.

1.4   E.g. Carbonation weathering *[1 mark]*.

Pages 34-35 — Coastal Landforms Caused by Erosion

1.1   Headland *[1 mark]*

1.2   Any two from: headlands have steep sides *[1 mark]*. / They jut out from the coastline *[1 mark]*. / They are made of resistant rock *[1 mark]*.

1.3   Headlands and bays form on discordant coastlines where there are alternating bands of resistant and less resistant rock along the coast *[1 mark]*. The less resistant rock is eroded quickly and this forms a bay *[1 mark]*. The resistant rock is eroded more slowly, forming a headland *[1 mark]*.

2.1   X is a wave-cut notch *[1 mark]*.
        Y is unstable/overhanging rock *[1 mark]*.

2.2   This question is level marked. How to grade your answer:
        Level 0:   There is no relevant information. *[0 marks]*
        Level 1:   There is a basic explanation of how wave-cut platforms are formed. *[1-2 marks]*
        Level 2:   There is a clear explanation of how wave-cut platforms are formed. *[3-4 marks]*
        Level 3:   There is a detailed explanation of how cliffs are undercut to form wave-cut notches and then wave-cut platforms. *[5-6 marks]*
    Here are some points your answer may include:
- Waves cause most erosion at the foot of a cliff.
- This forms a wave-cut notch (X on Figure 2).
- The notch is enlarged as erosion continues.
- As the notch grows, the rock above it becomes unstable (Y on Figure 2) and eventually collapses.
- The collapsed rock is washed away, leaving a wave-cut platform.

The question says 'Using Figure 2' so refer to the features you named for question 2.1. Describe each of the stages in the formation of wave-cut platforms, and make it clear how each stage leads on to the next.

3.1   Cave *[1 mark]*. It was formed when waves crashing into the headland enlarged cracks in the rock — mainly by hydraulic power and abrasion *[1 mark]*. Repeated erosion and enlargement of the cracks caused a cave to form *[1 mark]*.

3.2   One mark for arch correctly labelled.

3.3   The side of a headland is eroded by the sea to form a cave *[1 mark]*. Continued erosion deepens the cave until it breaks through the headland and forms an arch *[1 mark]*.

4.1   This question is level marked. How to grade your answer:
        Level 0:   There is no relevant information. *[0 marks]*
        Level 1:   There is a basic suggestion of what the coastal area may look like in the future. *[1-2 marks]*
        Level 2:   There is a clear suggestion of what the coastal area may look like in the future. *[3-4 marks]*
    Here are some points your answer may include:
- The rock supporting the arch could be eroded further, causing the arch to collapse and form a stack.
- The cave may be eroded further to form an arch.
- The bay may be eroded further, forming a deeper bay.

Page 36 — Coastal Transportation and Deposition

1.1   E.g. at 0 m, the beach was 5 m wider in 2010 than it was in 2015 *[1 mark]*. At 1000 m, the beach was 7-8 m narrower in 2010 than 2015 *[1 mark]*. The width of the beach varied by 5 m in 2010, but by much more in 2015 (17-18 m) *[1 mark]*.

1.2   This question is level marked. How to grade your answer:
        Level 0:   There is no relevant information. *[0 marks]*
        Level 1:   There is a basic description of longshore drift. *[1-2 marks]*
        Level 2:   Longshore drift is mentioned by name, and the process is clearly described. *[3-4 marks]*
    Here are some points your answer may include:
- The sediment was transported by longshore drift.
- Longshore drift is when waves follow the direction of the prevailing wind, which means they usually hit the coast at an oblique angle.
- The swash carries material up the beach, in the same direction as the waves.
- The backwash then carries material down the beach at right angles to the beach, back towards the sea.
- Over time, material zigzags along the coast.
- The beach becomes narrower where material is transported away and wider where material is deposited.

1.3   E.g. there's lots of erosion elsewhere on the coast, so there's lots of material available *[1 mark]*. / There's lots of transportation of material into the area *[1 mark]*.

1.4   Constructive waves *[1 mark]*.

1.5   Any two from: e.g. constructive waves are low frequency *[1 mark]*. / They are low and long *[1 mark]*. / They have a powerful swash *[1 mark]*. / They have a weak backwash *[1 mark]*.

Page 37 — Coastal Landforms Caused by Deposition

1.1   991802 *[1 mark]*

1.2   2.0 km (accept between 1.9 km and 2.1 km) *[1 mark]*

1.3   Longshore drift transported sand and shingle north east past a sharp bend in the coastline *[1 mark]* and deposited it in the sea, forming a spit *[1 mark]*.

1.4   The spit could continue to grow across the bay *[1 mark]*, creating a bar *[1 mark]*.

2.1   Sand blowing up the beach was trapped by obstacles, e.g. driftwood, forming embryo dunes *[1 mark]*. These small dunes were colonised by vegetation, trapping more sand and causing them to grow into foredunes and then mature dunes *[1 mark]*. New embryo dunes formed in front of these mature dunes *[1 mark]*.

Page 38 — Coastal Management Strategies

1.1   C *[1 mark]*

1.2   Any one from: e.g. beach nourishment is when sand and shingle from elsewhere or from lower down the beach is added to the upper part of beaches *[1 mark]*. / Dune regeneration is when sand dunes are created or restored by nourishment, or by planting vegetation to stabilise the sand *[1 mark]*.

1.3   Beach nourishment creates wider beaches which slow the waves, giving greater protection from flooding and erosion *[1 mark]*. / Dune regeneration restores or creates sand dunes that provide a barrier between the land and the sea. This means wave energy is absorbed, which prevents flooding and erosion *[1 mark]*.

1.4   E.g. 1: Taking material from the sea bed for beach nourishment can kill organisms like sponges and corals *[1 mark]*.
        2: Beach nourishment is also a very expensive defence that has to be repeated *[1 mark]*. /
        1: Dune regeneration only protects a small area *[1 mark]*.
        2: Nourishment of existing dunes is very expensive *[1 mark]*.

1.5   Cliffall is a town, so managed retreat would mean allowing homes and businesses to be lost to the sea *[1 mark]*. This would have large social and economic costs *[1 mark]*.

Unit 1: Living with the Physical Environment

1.6 This question is level marked. There are 3 extra marks available for spelling, punctuation and grammar.
How to grade your answer:

Level 0: There is no relevant information. *[0 marks]*
Level 1: There is a basic description of a management strategy. *[1-3 marks]*
Level 2: There is a clear description of a management strategy and a basic assessment of its success. *[4-6 marks]*
Level 3: There is a detailed description of a management strategy and a thorough assessment of its success, including its advantages and disadvantages. *[7-9 marks]*

Make sure your spelling, punctuation and grammar is consistently correct, that your meaning is clear and that you use a range of geographical terms correctly *[0-3 marks]*.
Your answer must outline a management strategy for a named area and describe ways in which it has been successful and ways in which it has caused problems. You must come to a conclusion about how successful it has been and explain your decision.
Here are some points your answer may include:
• Management strategies may include hard or soft engineering strategies, or managed retreat.
• Hard engineering strategies may include placing rock armour along the base of the cliff to absorb the power of the waves, or building rock groynes to trap sand and create a beach to slow the waves.
• Management strategy successes may include reduced rates of erosion, reduced frequency or magnitude of flood events, low costs, or new marshland habitats being created.
• Management strategy problems may include starved beaches or increased erosion rates further down the coast, high cost of installation, high cost of maintenance, environmental damage, the negative effect of saltwater on existing ecosystems or loss of farmland.
• Answers may refer to Lyme Regis in Dorset, where around 1 km of coastline is managed. This includes 390 m of sea walls and rock armour, which cost £19.5 million. The scheme has reduced erosion and protected the town, but defences may need rebuilding within 60 years.

Unit 1C — River Landscapes in the UK

Page 39 — The River Valley

1.1 B *[1 mark]*
The source is the start of the river, where it is at its highest point.
1.2 **Cross profile at point B:** The valley is V-shaped with steep sides *[1 mark]*. The channel is narrow and shallow *[1 mark]*.
Cross profile at point C: The valley is very wide and almost flat *[1 mark]*. The channel is very wide and deep *[1 mark]*.
1.3 This question is level marked. How to grade your answer:
Level 0: There is no relevant information. *[0 marks]*
Level 1: There is a basic description of vertical and lateral erosion and their effect on the cross profile. *[1-2 marks]*
Level 2: There is a clear explanation of the different types of erosion and their effects on the cross profile. *[3-4 marks]*
Here are some points your answer may include:
• In the upper course of the river, vertical erosion is dominant.
• Vertical erosion deepens the river valley (and channel), making it V-shaped.
• High turbulence in the upper course causes the rough, angular particles to be scraped along the river bed, causing intense downwards erosion.
• In the lower course of a river, lateral erosion is dominant.
• Lateral erosion widens the river valley (and channel) during the formation of meanders.

2.1 Any two from: the gradient of the river channel is steep *[1 mark]*. / The valley has steep sides *[1 mark]*. / The valley is V-shaped *[1 mark]*. / The river channel is narrow *[1 mark]*. / The river valley has interlocking spurs *[1 mark]*.

Page 40 — Erosion, Transportation and Deposition

1.1 10 km *[1 mark]*
1.2 0.8 metres per second *[1 mark]*
1.3 Saltation *[1 mark]*
You could also have said traction — pebbles will be rolled along the river bed before they start to saltate.
1.4 Between 20 and 30 km the river's velocity drops *[1 mark]*. When rivers slow down they have less energy so they deposit the material they are carrying *[1 mark]*.
1.5 The particle size generally decreases with distance from the river's source *[1 mark]*. This is because particles carried by the river bump into/collide with one another *[1 mark]* causing fragments to break off (this process is called attrition) *[1 mark]*.
1.6 Any two from: hydraulic action may deepen the river channel because the force of the water breaks rock particles away from the river bed *[1 mark]*. / Abrasion may deepen the river channel because eroded rocks picked up by the river scrape and rub against the river bed, wearing it away *[1 mark]*. / Solution may deepen the river channel because river water dissolves some types of rock, e.g. chalk and limestone *[1 mark]*.

Pages 41-43 — River Landforms

1.1 633524 *[1 mark]*
1.2 0.4 km *[1 mark]*
1.3 Waterfall Y *[1 mark]*
Remember that the steeper the gradient, the closer together the contour lines will be.
1.4 Waterfalls form where a river flows over an area of hard rock followed by an area of softer rock *[1 mark]*, so the Afon Merch must flow over rocks with alternating hardness *[1 mark]*.
1.5 A gorge forms as a waterfall retreats up a river channel *[1 mark]*. The hard rock cap is undercut by erosion (abrasion) so it becomes unsupported and collapses *[1 mark]*. Over time, more undercutting causes more collapses, so the waterfall retreats, forming a gorge *[1 mark]*.
2.1 This question is level marked. How to grade your answer:
Level 0: There is no relevant information. *[0 marks]*
Level 1: There is a basic explanation of the formation of interlocking spurs. *[1-2 marks]*
Level 2: There is a detailed explanation of the formation of interlocking spurs, which uses geographical terms accurately. *[3-4 marks]*
Here are some points your answer may include:
• In the upper course of a river most of the erosion is vertically downwards, creating steep-sided, V-shaped valleys.
• In the upper course, rivers aren't powerful enough to erode laterally (sideways), so they wind around the high hillsides that stick out into their paths on either side.
• The hillsides interlock with each other as the river winds around them, forming interlocking spurs.
3.1 A river cliff is likely to be found at A *[1 mark]*. The current is faster on the outside bend of the meander because the channel is deeper so there's less friction *[1 mark]*. This means there's more erosion on the outside bend, so a river cliff is formed *[1 mark]*.
3.2 A slip-off slope is likely to be found at B *[1 mark]*. The current is slower on the inside bend of the meander because the river channel is shallower so there's more friction *[1 mark]*. This means material is deposited on the inside of the bend, so a slip-off slope is formed *[1 mark]*.
3.3 The neck of the meander *[1 mark]*

Unit 1: Living with the Physical Environment

3.4 This question is level marked. How to grade your answer:

Level 0: There is no relevant information. *[0 marks]*

Level 1: There is a basic explanation of the formation of an ox-bow lake. *[1-2 marks]*

Level 2: There is a clear explanation of the formation of an ox-bow lake. *[3-4 marks]*

Level 3: There is a detailed explanation of the formation of an ox-bow lake, which uses geographical terms accurately. *[5-6 marks]*

Here are some points your answer may include:
- The current is fastest at the outside bend of a meander because the channel is deeper.
- The fast current at the outside bend means that more erosion takes place here, by the processes of abrasion and hydraulic action.
- Erosion causes the outside bends of a meander to get closer.
- The outside bends continue getting closer until there's only a small bit of land left between the bends (called the neck).
- The river breaks through the neck, usually during a flood, and flows along the shortest course.
- Material is deposited across the inlets to the old meander. This eventually cuts off the meander, forming an ox-bow lake.

4.1 A *[1 mark]*
Levees are natural embankments (raised sections) along the banks of the river.

4.2 During a flood, eroded material is deposited over the whole flood plain *[1 mark]*. The heaviest material is deposited closest to the river channel, because it gets dropped first when the river slows down *[1 mark]*. Over time, the deposited material builds up, creating levees along the edges of the channel *[1 mark]*.

4.3 When the river floods onto the flood plain, the water slows down and deposits the eroded material that it's transporting *[1 mark]*, so if the river floods repeatedly, the flood plain builds up *[1 mark]*.

5.1 This question is level marked. How to grade your answer:

Level 0: There is no relevant information. *[0 marks]*

Level 1: There is a basic explanation of the formation of an estuary. *[1-2 marks]*

Level 2: There is a clear explanation of the formation of an estuary, which uses some geographical terms. *[3-4 marks]*

Here are some points your answer may include:
- Estuaries are found at the mouth of a river, where the land is close to sea level.
- The water is tidal, so the river level rises and falls each day.
- When the tide comes in, the water floods over the banks of the river. At its highest point, the water has little energy, so it deposits silt and sand on the valley floor.
- Over time, more and more mud builds up, creating large areas of mudflats.

Page 44 — River Discharge and Flooding

1.1 20:00 on day 1 *[1 mark]*

1.2 18 hours *[1 mark]*

1.3 The River Seeton is more likely to flood *[1 mark]* because it has a higher peak discharge, meaning that there is more water in the channel *[1 mark]*. / The River Seeton is more likely to flood *[1 mark]* because it has a shorter lag time, meaning that discharge increases more quickly *[1 mark]*.

1.4 Built-up areas contain lots of impermeable surfaces and drains *[1 mark]*. Impermeable surfaces increase runoff and drains quickly take runoff to rivers, so the hydrograph will have a higher peak discharge and a shorter lag time *[1 mark]*.

1.5 Any two from: e.g. prolonged rainfall causes the soil to become saturated, so any further rainfall can't infiltrate *[1 mark]*. This increases runoff into the river, so discharge increases quickly and the river is more likely to flood *[1 mark]*. / Heavy rainfall means the water arrives too rapidly for infiltration, so there's a lot of runoff *[1 mark]*. This increases discharge quickly, so the risk of flooding increases *[1 mark]*. / Clay soils and some rocks, e.g. granite and shale, are impermeable (i.e. they don't allow infiltration) so runoff is increased *[1 mark]*. When it rains, discharge increases quickly, so the flood risk increases *[1 mark]*. / If a river is in a steep-sided valley, water will reach the river channel much faster because water flows more quickly on steeper slopes *[1 mark]*. Discharge increases rapidly, so flooding is more likely *[1 mark]*.

Page 45 — Hard vs Soft Engineering

1.1 Channel straightening *[1 mark]*.

1.2 Channel straightening may cause flooding or increased erosion at Fultow *[1 mark]* because flood water is carried there faster *[1 mark]*.

1.3 Flood plain zoning prevents people building on parts of a flood plain that are likely to flood *[1 mark]*. It reduces the risk of flooding because impermeable surfaces aren't created, e.g. buildings and roads *[1 mark]*. It also reduces the impact of flooding because there aren't any houses or roads to be damaged *[1 mark]*.

2.1 E.g. flood warnings don't stop a flood from happening *[1 mark]*. / Some people may not hear or have access to warnings *[1 mark]*.

2.2 Warnings give people time to move possessions upstairs, put sandbags in position and to evacuate *[1 mark]*. This means that there is less damage to property and less risk to people *[1 mark]*.

2.3 This question is level marked. There are 3 extra marks available for spelling, punctuation and grammar. How to grade your answer:

Level 0: There is no relevant information. *[0 marks]*

Level 1: There is a basic description of a management strategy. *[1-3 marks]*

Level 2: There is a clear description of a management strategy and a basic assessment of its success. *[4-6 marks]*

Level 3: There is a detailed description of a management strategy and a thorough assessment of its success, including its advantages and disadvantages. *[7-9 marks]*

Make sure your spelling, punctuation and grammar is consistently correct, that your meaning is clear and that you use a range of geographical terms correctly *[0-3 marks]*.
Your answer must refer to a specific example.
Here are some points your answer may include:
- A brief description of the reasons why the management strategy was required.
- A detailed description of the strategy, including the hard engineering defences used (e.g. dams, embankments, channel straightening) as well as the soft engineering strategies used (e.g. flood plain zoning, flood warnings, planting trees).
- An assessment of the advantages and disadvantages of the management strategy, e.g. its effectiveness at reducing the flood risk, its effects on the character of the area, the cost, the impact on the environment etc.
- A conclusion as to how successful the strategy has been.
- Your answer may refer to Oxford's flood management scheme. The scheme, which started being planned in 2014, involves building new flood walls and planting trees to decrease peak discharge. The scheme will protect over 1000 homes and businesses, but it will cost over £120 million.

Unit 1: Living with the Physical Environment

Unit 1C — Glacial Landscapes in the UK

Pages 46-47: Glacial Erosion and Landforms

1.1   B *[1 mark]*
An arête is a narrow, steep-sided ridge. Look at the really thin hill with tightly packed, parallel contours on either side. Its name, 'Striding Edge', is a clue too.

1.2   **Grid reference:** 3614 *[1 mark]*.
         Formation: Glacial troughs start off as V-shaped river valleys *[1 mark]*. Glaciers erode the sides and bottom of the valley, forming a U-shaped glacial trough *[1 mark]*.

1.3   1.7 km (allow 1.6-1.8km) *[1 mark]*

1.4   Corrie *[1 mark]*
You may also have called this feature a cwm or a cirque — these are correct too.

1.5   A corrie begins as a hollow containing a small glacier *[1 mark]*. As the ice moves by rotational slip *[1 mark]*, it erodes the hollow into a steep-sided, armchair shape with a lip at the bottom end *[1 mark]*.

1.6   Helvellyn *[1 mark]*

2.1   D *[1 mark]*
Hanging valleys are smaller valleys that are left at a higher level than the main valley when the ice melts, appearing to 'hang' above them.

2.2   Hanging valleys are valleys formed by smaller tributary glaciers that flow into the main glacier *[1 mark]*. The glacial trough is eroded much more deeply by the larger glacier *[1 mark]*, so when the glaciers melt, the valleys of the tributary glaciers are left at a higher level *[1 mark]*.

2.3   1: Plucking occurs when meltwater at the base, back or sides of a glacier freezes onto the rock *[1 mark]*. As the glacier moves forward it pulls pieces of rock off the mountain face, making the back wall steeper *[1 mark]*.
         2: Abrasion occurs when bits of rock stuck in the ice grind against the rock below the glacier, wearing it away *[1 mark]*. Abrasion wears away rock at the base of the glacier, making the base deeper and forming the hollow between X and Y (which is now a tarn) *[1 mark]*.
You may have also described how the glacier moves in a circular motion (called rotational slip) as part of your answer. This erodes hollows in the landscape like the one shown in the photo.

2.4   It may have been weathered by freeze-thaw weathering, where water gets into cracks in rocks, freezes and expands, putting pressure on the rock *[1 mark]*. The ice then thaws, releasing the pressure *[1 mark]*. If this process is repeated it can make bits of the rock break off/shatter *[1 mark]*.

Page 48: Glacial Transportation and Deposition

1.1   A *[1 mark]*
Medial moraine is a ridge of material deposited along the centre of a valley.

1.2   Any one from: the material can be frozen in the glacier *[1 mark]*. / The material can be carried on the surface of the glacier *[1 mark]*. / The material can be transported by bulldozing, when the ice pushes loose material in front of it *[1 mark]*.

1.3   Terminal moraine forms at the snout of the glacier *[1 mark]*. Material is abraded and plucked from the valley floor and transported at the front of the glacier *[1 mark]*. When the ice retreats, the material is deposited as semicircular mounds *[1 mark]*.

2.1

Scale: 0   200 m

[1 mark]

2.2   Drumlins are elongated hills *[1 mark]* which are round, blunt and steep at the upstream end and tapered, pointed and gently sloping at the downstream end *[1 mark]*. The drumlin in Figure 2 is about 1000 m long, 58 m tall and 500 m wide *[1 mark]*.

Page 49: Land Use in Glacial Landscapes

1.1   Either:
         Land use: Forestry *[1 mark]*
         Reason: Coniferous forests are often planted in upland areas because they can cope with the cold weather and high rainfall *[1 mark]*. The trees are used for timber, e.g. for building materials *[1 mark]*.
         Or:
         Land use: Quarrying *[1 mark]*
         Reason: The erosion by glaciers left lots of rock exposed, making it easy to get to *[1 mark]*. Glacial landscapes are often quarried for slate, granite, and limestone *[1 mark]*.
There's also a wind turbine in the background of the picture, so you might have chosen to write about that instead.

1.2   This question is level marked. How to grade your answer:
         Level 0:   There is no relevant information. *[0 marks]*
         Level 1:   There is a basic description of at least one conflict caused by forestry. *[1-2 marks]*
         Level 2:   There is a detailed description and explanation of more than one conflict caused by forestry in glacial landscapes. *[3-4 marks]*
         Here are some points your answer may include:
         • Harvesting trees means chopping forests down, which creates conflict with conservationists. This is because it can scare off wildlife and damage habitats.
         • Forestry plantations are often made up of coniferous trees, which don't support as many different types of species as mixed woodland. This creates conflict with conservationists.
         • Lower biodiversity may make the area less attractive to tourists, causing conflict with people employed in the tourism industry.
         • There may also be limited access for tourists while the trees are being chopped down.

1.3   Any one from: tourism *[1 mark]* / farming *[1 mark]*

1.4   This question is level marked. How to grade your answer:
         Level 0:   There is no relevant information. *[0 marks]*
         Level 1:   There is a basic description of some of the problems caused by development in glacial landscapes. *[1-2 marks]*
         Level 2:   There is a clear outline of the problems caused by development and attempt to balance them with some benefits. *[3-4 marks]*
         Level 3:   There is a detailed description of the problems caused by development and the answer draws a justified conclusion by balancing the problems with potential benefits. *[5-6 marks]*
         Here are some points your answer may include:
         • Development of glacial landscapes can bring benefits to the area. For example, it provides employment (e.g. in farming, quarrying, forestry or tourism) and provides roads and facilities for the many visitors to glacial areas as well as the local communities.
         • Development brings money into the area, which means that services will improve, e.g. more frequent buses, more shops etc. This will improve the quality of life of the people who live there.
         • However, there can be conflicts between different forms of development. For example, quarrying makes the environment less attractive to tourists so they may be discouraged from visiting. This could have economic impacts on local businesses that depend on the tourists.

Answers

Unit 2: Challenges in the Human Environment

• There may be conflicts between development and conservation of glacial landscapes. For example, conservationists want to preserve the environmental value of the landscapes, but development can damage the environment and destroy habitats.

Your answer should weigh up the benefits and problems caused by development, and come to a conclusion about their relative importance.

Page 50: Tourism in Glacial Landscapes

1.1   90 *[1 mark]*
1.2   There are plenty of activities for people to do, e.g. walking, rock climbing, cycling, canoeing *[1 mark]*. There is attractive scenery for people to visit, e.g. ribbon lakes and mountains *[1 mark]*.
1.3   Any one from: e.g. tourism is often the main industry, providing income to the area *[1 mark]*. / Tourism offers employment to local people (e.g. in hotels, shops, cafés and the outdoor industry) *[1 mark]*.
1.4   This question is level marked. How to grade your answer:
Level 0:   There is no relevant information. *[0 marks]*
Level 1:   There is a basic description of some of the negative impacts of tourists on national parks in glacial landscapes. *[1-2 marks]*
Level 2:   There is a clear description of the negative impacts of tourists on national parks in glacial landscapes. *[3-4 marks]*
Here are some points your answer may include:
• Figure 1 shows the number of tourists is increasing, so the problems they cause are likely to be getting worse.
• Economic problems, e.g. house prices are often high due to demand for holiday homes and second homes. This can mean that local people cannot afford to buy houses and are forced to move out of the area.
• Social problems, e.g. holiday homes are not occupied all year round. This can lead to some services for local residents being limited, for example, reduced bus services in off-peak seasons. Figure 1 also shows that a greater number of tourists can increase the risk of people being involved in traffic accidents.
• Environmental problems, e.g. footpath erosion is often a problem due to the large numbers of walkers. Vegetation is destroyed and exposed soil is washed away. This damages the landscape and leaves large erosion scars.
1.5   The park has put a 40 mph speed limit on the roads, to reduce the number of traffic accidents involving tourists *[1 mark]*.
1.6   Any two from: e.g. resurface paths with hard-wearing materials, e.g. rocks, plastic mesh, slabs, etc. to reduce erosion *[1 mark]*. / Re-seed vegetation to reduce the visual impact of footpath erosion *[1 mark]*. / Encourage visitors to stick to marked routes by providing signposting or fencing *[1 mark]*. / Increase public transport in the tourist season to reduce traffic congestion *[1 mark]*. / Improve the road network, e.g. by providing passing places on single-track roads, to reduce traffic congestion *[1 mark]*. / Encourage people to use bikes, buses, boats and trains, e.g. by providing discounts, to reduce congestion and pollution *[1 mark]*. / Use signs to remind people to take their litter home and provide covered bins at the most popular sites *[1 mark]*. / Encourage visitors to enjoy the countryside responsibly, e.g. by reminding them to close gates and keep dogs on leads *[1 mark]*.

Section 2A — Urban Issues and Challenges

Pages 51-52: Urbanisation

1.1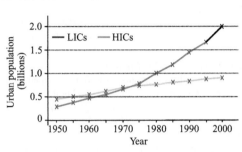
[1 mark]
1.2   The urban population of HICs increased gradually from about 0.5 billion to 0.9 billion *[1 mark]*. The urban population of LICs was less than that of HICs in 1950 but much greater by 2000 *[1 mark]*. It increased rapidly from about 0.3 billion to 2 billion *[1 mark]*.
1.3   Urbanisation is the growth in the proportion of people living in **urban** *[1 mark]* areas. It is caused by natural increase and by the migration of people from **rural** *[1 mark]* areas. People leave such areas because of push factors, including e.g. **natural disasters** *[1 mark]* / **fewer jobs** *[1 mark]* / **difficulty of growing food** *[1 mark]* / **conflict** *[1 mark]*.
1.4   Any two from: e.g. there are more jobs in urban areas, and they are often better paid *[1 mark]*. / To get access to better health care and education *[1 mark]*. / To join other family members who have already moved *[1 mark]*. / People think they will have a better quality of life in cities *[1 mark]*.
1.5   Natural increase is when the birth rate is higher than the death rate, so the population grows *[1 mark]*. It's normally young people that move to cities to find work *[1 mark]*. These people then have children in the cities, which increases the proportion of the population living in urban areas *[1 mark]*.
1.6   This question is level marked. How to grade your answer:
Level 0:   There is no relevant information. *[0 marks]*
Level 1:   There are a few points about the rate of urbanisation in either HICs or LICs. *[1-2 marks]*
Level 2:   There is a clear explanation of the rate of urbanisation in HICs and LICs. *[3-4 marks]*
Level 3:   There is a detailed explanation of the rate of urbanisation in HICs and LICs. *[5-6 marks]*
Here are some points your answer may include:
• Urbanisation happened earlier in HICs than in LICs, so the majority of the population already live in urban areas. This means that there are fewer people moving into cities in HICs than in LICs.
• Good transport and communication networks mean that people in HICs can live in rural areas and commute to cities, or work from home. This means that many people in HICs are moving away from cities.
• Decline of heavy industry in cities in HICs caused mass unemployment. People desiring a better quality of life moved away from overcrowded cities to rural areas, meaning that urban population growth slowed.
• A lower proportion of the population in LICs currently live in urban areas, so there are more people living in rural areas who might move to cities.
• Many people in LICs are moving to cities to get a better quality of life, e.g. access to better healthcare, jobs and education. This causes rapid urban growth in LICs.
2.1   C *[1 mark]*
Make sure you learn the meaning of geographical words — megacities are defined as having a population of more than 10 million people.

Unit 2: Challenges in the Human Environment

2.2 The number of megacities increased from three in 1975 to twenty-eight in 2014 *[1 mark]*. By 2014 there were a few more megacities in HICs and LICs *[1 mark]*. However, most of the new megacities that had developed by 2014 are in NEEs *[1 mark]*.

Page 53: Urban Growth — Opportunities and Challenges

1.1 Any two from: e.g. Figure 1 shows children in school uniform — cities offer better access to services such as education compared to rural areas *[1 mark]*. / Figure 1 shows electricity and telephone cables connecting buildings — cities offer better access to resources such as electricity *[1 mark]*. / There are motorbikes parked outside the buildings in Figure 1, showing that people are reasonably wealthy — cities offer more jobs and better wages than rural areas *[1 mark]*.

The question tells you to use the figure, so make sure you comment on opportunities you can identify from the photo.

1.2 Any two from: e.g. rubbish often isn't collected or it may end up in big rubbish heaps *[1 mark]*. / Air pollution comes from burning fuel, vehicle exhaust fumes and factories *[1 mark]*. / Sewage and toxic chemicals from factories can get into rivers, harming wildlife *[1 mark]*. / Traffic congestion from rapidly increasing numbers of cars causes increased greenhouse gas emissions *[1 mark]*.

1.3 This question is level marked. How to grade your answer:
Level 0: There is no relevant information. *[0 marks]*
Level 1: There is a basic explanation of some positive effects of a named urban planning scheme in an LIC or NEE. *[1-2 marks]*
Level 2: There is a clear explanation of the positive effects of a named urban planning scheme in an LIC or NEE. *[3-4 marks]*
Your answer must refer to a named example.
Here are some points your answer may include:
• A brief description of the area and why the scheme was required.
• A description of any social improvements, e.g. better access to health care, education, electricity, clean water supply and improved sanitation, and an explanation of how these have a positive effect, e.g. improving people's health and skills.
• A description of any economic improvements, e.g. training to allow people access to better jobs, and an explanation of how these have a positive effect, e.g. giving people higher wages and a better quality of life.
• A description of any environmental improvements, e.g. improving the sewer system, using renewable energy to decrease pollution and introducing rubbish collection schemes, and an explanation of how these have a positive effect, e.g. by making the area more pleasant and healthier to live in.
• Answers may refer to the Makoko Floating School, which provided a free education for up to 100 students at a time, employed local workers and was powered by solar energy.

1.4 This question is level marked. There are 3 extra marks available for spelling, punctuation and grammar.
How to grade your answer:
Level 0: There is no relevant information. *[0 marks]*
Level 1: There is a basic description of the challenges created by urban growth. *[1-3 marks]*
Level 2: There is a clear discussion of the challenges of urban growth. *[4-6 marks]*
Level 3: There is a detailed discussion of the challenges created by urban growth. *[7-9 marks]*
Make sure your spelling, punctuation and grammar is consistently correct, that your meaning is clear and that you use a range of geographical terms correctly *[0-3 marks]*.
Your answer must refer to a named example.

Here are some points your answer may include:
• A brief description of the city in an LIC or NEE that you have chosen and how it is growing.
• A discussion of the social challenges caused by urban growth, e.g. the growth of squatter settlements with poorly built, overcrowded housing. Your answer should describe some of the problems this creates, including limited access to healthcare, education, clean water, electricity and sanitary facilities and high levels of crime.
• A discussion of the economic challenges caused by urban growth, including a lack of formal jobs and high levels of unemployment. Many formal jobs (e.g. in factories) have long working hours and low pay.
• A discussion of the environmental challenges caused by urban growth, including lack of proper sewage systems and waste collection services, air pollution from traffic congestion and unregulated waste disposal and emissions from factories.
• Your answer may refer to the city of Lagos, Nigeria, which is experiencing rapid urban growth. 66% of the population live in squatter settlements without access to basic services or resources.

Page 54: UK Cities

1.1 The west and north of the UK generally have a low population density *[1 mark]*. Population density is highest in the south east and the midlands *[1 mark]*.

1.2 A: Glasgow *[1 mark]*
B: London *[1 mark]*

1.3 Upland regions such as the north of Scotland are difficult to farm and have few natural resources *[1 mark]*.

2.1 Any two from: e.g. the buildings have been improved *[1 mark]*. / A walkway has been developed along the river *[1 mark]*. / New homes/offices have been built *[1 mark]*. / The environment has been made more attractive *[1 mark]*.

2.2 This question is level marked. How to grade your answer:
Level 0: There is no relevant information. *[0 marks]*
Level 1: There is a basic explanation of the improvements made to a named UK regeneration project. *[1-2 marks]*
Level 2: There is a clear explanation of the improvements made to a named UK regeneration project. *[3-4 marks]*
Your answer must refer to a named example.
Here are some points your answer may include:
• A brief description of the regeneration project and why the area needed regenerating.
• Social improvements, such as better (and affordable) housing, community facilities (health care centres, community centres etc.) and the introduction of services such as cafés and shops.
• Economic improvements, such as the creation of jobs and improved transport links.
• Environmental improvements, such as the development of parks and community sports fields, and the cleaning up of waste land.
• Your answer may refer to the Anfield Project, which aimed to regenerate the Anfield area of Liverpool. The project refurbished derelict homes to improve quality of life for residents. It also improved community facilities, such as the sports centre, and outdoor areas, including Stanley Park.

Unit 2: Challenges in the Human Environment

Page 55: Change in UK Cities

1.1 E.g. derelict buildings became a target for crime and graffiti *[1 mark]*. / Areas in many inner cities became deprived, with poor access to health care, education and a lack of job opportunities *[1 mark]*.

1.2 Any two from: e.g. the combination of accents from different groups of immigrants may have contributed to Liverpool's distinctive 'scouse' accent *[1 mark]*. / Many immigrants set up their own communities within the city, for example, Chinatown. *[1 mark]*. / Migration has made the city culturally diverse with a range of foods, festivals and cultural experiences *[1 mark]*.

1.3 E.g. in Liverpool, planners are trying to increase and preserve open spaces such as public parks and gardens *[1 mark]*. More cycle and pedestrian routes are being created and wasteland is being converted into usable parks, e.g. Chavasse Park, which is right in the middle of the city centre *[1 mark]*.

1.4 This question is level marked. How to grade your answer:
Level 0: There is no relevant information. *[0 marks]*
Level 1: There is a basic explanation of the effect of urban sprawl on the rural-urban fringe. *[1-2 marks]*
Level 2: There is a clear explanation of the effect of urban sprawl on the rural-urban fringe. *[3-4 marks]*
Your answer must refer to a named example.
Here are some points your answer may include:
• A brief description of how the city has spread.
• An explanation of the positive effects of urban sprawl on the rural-urban fringe, such as new housing estates with lots of green space providing a pleasant environment for people living there; opportunities to build airports, out-of-town shopping centres, golf courses etc. because the land is cheaper and less built-up than in the town centre.
• An explanation of the negative effects of urban sprawl on the rural-urban fringe, such as the loss of farmland and green space, and damage to ecosystems; traffic congestion and air pollution from increased commuting distances and more commuters; spoiling of character of rural villages that get incorporated into the sprawling urban area.
• Your answer may refer to the sprawling of Liverpool to create the Merseyside conurbation. This includes large housing estates, e.g. Croxteth Park, and out-of-town developments, e.g. Knowsley Business Park.

1.5 This question is level marked. There are 3 extra marks available for spelling, punctuation and grammar.
How to grade your answer:
Level 0: There is no relevant information. *[0 marks]*
Level 1: There is a basic description of some challenges and/or opportunities caused by urban change. *[1-3 marks]*
Level 2: There is some discussion of the challenges and opportunities caused by urban change and some attempt to come to a conclusion. *[4-6 marks]*
Level 3: There is a detailed discussion of the challenges and opportunities caused by urban change and the answer comes to a clear conclusion. *[7-9 marks]*
Make sure your spelling, punctuation and grammar is consistently correct, that your meaning is clear and that you use a range of geographical terms correctly *[0-3 marks]*.
Your answer must present both challenges and opportunities in a named UK city. You must decide whether the challenges or opportunities are more significant and justify your decision.
Here are some points your answer may include:
• A brief description of how the city has changed.
• A discussion of the challenges this change has presented. This may include social and economic challenges, e.g. urban deprivation leading to inequalities in housing, education, health and employment. It may also include environmental challenges, such as buildings and land being left derelict, the loss of greenfield land due to new developments, and the difficulties of waste disposal.

• A discussion of the opportunities the change has presented. This may include social and economic opportunities, e.g. a greater mix of cultures and more possibilities for recreation and entertainment; different employment opportunities; the development of integrated transport systems. It may also include environmental opportunities, such as urban greening, for example, the creation of parks and community woodlands and the development of cycle ways and footpaths.
• Your answer may also discuss the effects of urban sprawl on the environment and on the character of the settlements in the rural-urban fringe.
• Your answer may refer to Liverpool, a city in north west England that has changed from a deprived, former industrial city to a modern tourist destination and centre for creative industries.

Page 56: Sustainable Urban Living

1.1 E.g. there is lots of green space, including parks, wooded areas, rivers and lakes *[1 mark]*. / There is a big recycling centre *[1 mark]*.

1.2 This question is level marked. How to grade your answer:
Level 0: There is no relevant information. *[0 marks]*
Level 1: There is a basic explanation of how the feature identified makes the town more sustainable. *[1-2 marks]*
Level 2: There is a clear explanation of how the feature identified makes the town more sustainable. *[3-4 marks]*
You could have chosen to write about either green space or recycling facilities. Here are some points your answer may include:
Green space
• Cities can be noisy, dirty, busy and hot — they are unsustainable because people can find them unpleasant and stressful.
• Creating green space within urban areas helps to make sure that they remain places where people want to live and work.
• Green space can have social benefits, e.g. it provides naturally cooler areas where people can relax in hot weather, so it improves their quality of life.
• Green space can have environmental benefits, e.g. it reduces the risk of flooding by reducing surface runoff from rainfall.
Recycling centre
• More recycling means fewer resources are used.
• Having a recycling centre means that less waste goes to landfill. Landfill is unsustainable as it wastes resources that could be recycled and eventually there'll be nowhere left to bury the waste.
• Decomposing landfill releases greenhouse gases, which contribute to climate change. Increasing recycling therefore reduces the environmental impact of cities.
• Recycling facilities may mean that larger items, e.g. fridges, that are not taken away by waste collection services can be recycled rather than going to landfill.

1.3 This question is level marked. How to grade your answer:
Level 0: There is no relevant information. *[0 marks]*
Level 1: There is a basic explanation of how water can be conserved in people's homes. *[1-2 marks]*
Level 2: There is a clear explanation of how water can be conserved in people's homes. *[3-4 marks]*
Here are some points your answer may include:
• Houses could be fitted with water butts to collect rainwater for use on gardens or for flushing toilets, which reduces the amount of piped water needed.
• Toilets could be installed that use less water to flush.
• Water meters could be installed so that people have to pay for the water that they use. This is likely to reduce their water usage.

Unit 2: Challenges in the Human Environment

1.4 This question is level marked. How to grade your answer:
Level 0: There is no relevant information. *[0 marks]*
Level 1: There is a basic explanation of at least one energy conservation scheme. *[1-2 marks]*
Level 2: There is a clear explanation of a range of energy conservation schemes. *[3-4 marks]*
Here are some points your answer may include:
- Energy conservation schemes reduce the use of fossil fuels — fossil fuels are not sustainable because they emit greenhouse gases and they will run out.
- Energy conservation schemes can promote renewable energy sources (wind, solar, tidal etc.) over traditional coal- or gas-fired power stations.
- Government incentives to make homes more energy-efficient can be introduced, e.g. allowing homeowners who generate electricity from renewable sources (such as solar panels) to sell any excess energy to the national grid.
- New homes can be built to meet minimum energy efficiency requirements, so they use less power.
- Energy conservation schemes can encourage people to use less energy at home, e.g. by turning off lights.

Page 57: Traffic Management

1.1 Any two from: e.g. a higher chance of accidents (with other cars, cyclists, or pedestrians) *[1 mark]* / frustration for drivers *[1 mark]* / health issues for pedestrians and cyclists (from breathing in polluted air) *[1 mark]* / delayed emergency vehicles *[1 mark]*
1.2 This question is level marked. How to grade your answer:
Level 0: There is no relevant information. *[0 marks]*
Level 1: There is a basic description of some of the changes in transport links. *[1-2 marks]*
Level 2: There is a clear description and explanation of the changes in transport links. *[3-4 marks]*
Level 3: There is a detailed description and explanation of the changes in transport links. *[5-6 marks]*
Here are some points your answer may include:
- There are more railway stations, which means more people can easily access trains. This means that there should be fewer cars on the road.
- There is a new tram line connecting parts of the city without a rail connection. This will mean more people can travel by tram to the city centre so there should be fewer cars on the road.
- There is a new ring road, which should keep traffic away from the city centre, making it safer and less polluted, and preventing congestion on city centre roads.
- There are two new Park and Ride facilities. These allow people to drive to a large car park, then get the bus into the city centre. This means that fewer people need to take their cars into the city centre.
- There is a motorway running to the south of the town with two junctions. This means that people don't need to go through the city centre of Hamslow unless it is their destination.
1.3 Any two from: e.g. self-service bicycles could be used to encourage people to use public transport because they are cheap *[1 mark]*. / Pre-paid cards could be used to make it quicker and easier to use public transport *[1 mark]*. / Bus-priority lanes could be installed, meaning that buses don't get held up in traffic, making them a more attractive option than driving *[1 mark]*. / Parking restrictions could be used to make sure parked cars don't block traffic *[1 mark]*. / Congestion charging could be used to discourage people from driving into the city centre *[1 mark]*.

Unit 2B — The Changing Economic World

Page 58: Measuring Development

1.1 LICs are mostly found in the southern hemisphere *[1 mark]* and most are in Africa *[1 mark]*.
2.1 This question is level marked. How to grade your answer:
Level 0: There is no relevant information. *[0 marks]*
Level 1: There is a basic understanding of measures of development. Some application of knowledge in agreeing or disagreeing with the given statement. *[1-2 marks]*
Level 2: There is a clear understanding of measures of development. Good application of knowledge and a clearly justified agreement or disagreement with the statement. *[3-4 marks]*
Here are some points your answer may include:
- Canada has a much greater GNI per head than the other countries, which indicates that its citizens are wealthier, and can probably afford a high quality of life.
- Malaysia has a lower death rate than Canada, but other measures of health, such as infant mortality rate and life expectancy both indicate that Canada is more developed than Malaysia. Infants are less likely to die, and people have a longer life expectancy overall. This suggests that Canada has a developed and successful healthcare system.
- Canada's literacy rate is higher than Malaysia's, and much higher than Angola's. It suggests that there is a formal education system, and that children aren't required to work long hours on family farms, and so have the time to go to school. This suggests that Canada is the most developed of the three countries.
2.2 E.g. GNI per head is an average, so it can hide variation between regions in the country, and between classes *[1 mark]*. A country can have a large number of very poor people, but a small number of very wealthy people will skew the average *[1 mark]*.
2.3 E.g. individual indicators can be misleading if they are used on their own because as a country develops, some aspects develop before others *[1 mark]*. HDI is calculated using several different indicators, so it is likely to give a much more accurate idea of how developed a country is *[1 mark]*.

Page 59: Development and the DTM

1.1 A *[1 mark]* and D *[1 mark]*.
In Stage 5, birth rate is lower than death rate, so population decreases. In Stage 4, birth rate and death rate are equal, so population remains stable.
1.2 Any one from: e.g. poor healthcare *[1 mark]* / poor nutrition *[1 mark]*
1.3 Economic development means that women have a more equal place in society and better education, so birth rate falls *[1 mark]*. More women work instead of having children and the use of contraception increases *[1 mark]*. The birth rate also decreases because agriculture becomes a less important part of the economy, so fewer children are needed to work on farms *[1 mark]*.
1.4 Morocco has a relatively high birth rate and a low death rate *[1 mark]*, so it is likely to be at Stage 3 of the demographic transition model *[1 mark]*. Countries at Stage 3 are poorer countries, but with increasing levels of economic development *[1 mark]*.

Unit 2: Challenges in the Human Environment

Pages 60-61: Causes and Consequences of Uneven Development

1.1   E.g. conflict is likely to decrease Libya's level of development *[1 mark]*. This is because damage is done to infrastructure and property, such as the building in Figure 1 *[1 mark]*, and money is spent on arms and fighting instead of development *[1 mark]*.

1.2   Countries that were colonised often have a lower level of development when they gain independence than they would if they had not been colonised *[1 mark]*. This is because colonisers often remove raw materials and sell back manufactured goods *[1 mark]*. This means that more money goes to the colonising country, so it is not used to develop the colonised country, which remains relatively undeveloped *[1 mark]*.

1.3   If nearby countries have a higher level of development, Libyan people may seek to enter that country to improve their quality of life *[1 mark]*. So neighbouring countries may receive lots of Libyan migrants and refugees *[1 mark]*.

2.1   US $2.1 million *[1 mark]*
$5\ 100\ 000 \div 100 \times 41.4 = US\ \$2\ 111\ 400$.

2.2   78.3% *[1 mark]*
Manufactured and other products are left. $69.4 + 8.9 = 78.3$.

2.3   If a country has poor trade links (it trades a small amount with only a few countries) its GNI will be lower than if it had good trade links *[1 mark]*. This means there will be less to spend on development, so development will be slow *[1 mark]*.

2.4   Nicaragua's largest exports are agricultural products (which are primary products), and manufactured goods make up less of its exports than in the UK *[1 mark]*. Primary products don't generate as much money as manufactured goods, which means there is less money to spend on development in Nicaragua *[1 mark]*.

2.5   The health of people in the UK is likely to be better than in Nicaragua *[1 mark]*. Life expectancy is normally higher in more developed countries, and infant mortality is generally lower *[1 mark]*. Health improves with development, so the difference is likely to be a result of more investment in healthcare in the UK *[1 mark]*.

Pages 62-63: Reducing the Global Development Gap

1.1   £380 *[1 mark]*
Accept £370 to £390.

1.2   £260 *[1 mark]*
£490 − £230 = £260. Accept £250 to £270.

1.3   This question is level marked. How to grade your answer:

Level 0:   There is no relevant information. *[0 marks]*

Level 1:   There is a basic discussion of how fair trade schemes can increase a country's development. *[1-2 marks]*

Level 2:   There is a clear discussion of how fair trade schemes can increase a country's development. *[3-4 marks]*

Here are some points your answer may include:
- The farmer's income in Figure 1 rose quickly after he joined the fair trade cooperative, and continued to rise after that.
- His income may have increased because fair trade schemes involve paying farmers a fair price for goods produced.
- Receiving a fair price for goods means farmers' incomes increase, so they have more money to spend on improving their quality of life, which increases development.
- The extra money earned by the farmers can be spent in the country they live in, so others benefit too.
- The income of the state increases too through taxes, so there may be more investment in e.g. infrastructure and healthcare.

2.1   Any one from: e.g. tourism can provide extra employment *[1 mark]*, providing people with an income they might not have had otherwise *[1 mark]*. / Tourism contributes to a country's income *[1 mark]*, allowing it to invest in improving development and quality of life *[1 mark]*. / Entry fees can be charged for tourist attractions such as national parks *[1 mark]*, which fund preservation or protection schemes *[1 mark]*.

2.2   Any two from: e.g. most of the income from tourists goes to large, international companies based in HICs overseas *[1 mark]*, so the effect on development can be small *[1 mark]*. / Local people can be forced to move from land that is wanted for tourism, e.g. national parks *[1 mark]*, so they lose their homes and livelihoods *[1 mark]*. / Tourism vehicles can damage the environment *[1 mark]*, e.g. safari vehicles can destroy vegetation and disturb animals *[1 mark]*.

3.1   C *[1 mark]*
The aid is long-term because it is to help with Ghana's development and is not in response to an emergency. It is top-down because the money is being given to the Ghanaian government, not directly to the local people.

3.2   Advantage: e.g. helps to improve the level of development of the recipient country (by improving health, education and agriculture) *[1 mark]*.
Disadvantage: e.g. the aid may not reach the poorest people *[1 mark]* / aid may be lost through corruption *[1 mark]*.

3.3   Advantage: e.g. helps provide immediate disaster relief in recipient countries *[1 mark]*.
Disadvantage: e.g. often doesn't help with long-term recovery efforts *[1 mark]* / doesn't help improve overall level of development *[1 mark]*.

3.4   This question is level marked. There are 3 extra marks available for spelling, punctuation and grammar.
How to grade your answer:

Level 0:   There is no relevant information. *[0 marks]*

Level 1:   There is a basic description of how TNCs can affect economic development and quality of life in LICs and NEEs. *[1-3 marks]*

Level 2:   There is a clear description of the advantages and disadvantages of TNCs for economic development and quality of life in LICs and NEEs, and a basic judgement of the extent of improvements in a named country. *[4-6 marks]*

Level 3:   There is a detailed description of the advantages and disadvantages of TNCs for economic development and quality of life in LICs and NEEs, and a clear judgement of the extent of improvements in a named country. *[7-9 marks]*

Make sure your spelling, punctuation and grammar is consistently correct, that your meaning is clear and that you use a range of geographical terms correctly *[0-3 marks]*.

Your answer must outline ways in which TNCs can improve economic development and quality of life, and ways in which they do not generate improvements, using examples of TNCs in at least one country. You must come to a conclusion about how far they can improve economic development and quality of life, and explain your decision.

Here are some points your answer may include:
- TNCs help increase economic development and improve quality of life by employing people, which provides an income for workers and tax income for the state. Some TNCs also run programs to help development, and work with charities to help improve quality of life.
- TNCs may not help to improve economic development and quality of life as profits made by the company normally leave the country in which they were made. TNCs may also move around within countries or internationally to take advantage of local government incentives, which can reduce the income from TNCs or prevent long-term development.
- Some TNCs may also cause environmental damage, particularly if environmental regulations are not strict or not enforced. This can affect places where people live, which negatively affects quality of life.
- Answers may refer to TNCs in India. For example, Unilever employs over 16 000 people in India and runs development initiatives there, but much of its profit leaves India. TNCs add to environmental problems in India, such as air and water pollution, and some clothing manufacturers have been accused of paying low wages.

Unit 2: Challenges in the Human Environment

Page 64-66: Economic Development in the UK

1.1 Instead of a factory, there are now large office blocks *[1 mark]*. In common with the rest of the UK, manufacturing has become less important to Newcastle's economy *[1 mark]*. Office-based tertiary and quaternary industry, such as IT, finance, retail and research, have become much more important *[1 mark]*.

1.2 Any one from: e.g. de-industrialisation has meant that manufacturing and heavy industries have declined *[1 mark]*. / Globalisation has meant that a lot of manufacturing has moved overseas, where labour costs are lower *[1 mark]*. / Membership of groups such as the World Trade Organisation makes it easier for companies in the UK to operate across the world *[1 mark]*. / Secondary industries, e.g. manufacturing, have moved to the outskirts of cities where there is space to expand and where there is easier access for lorries *[1 mark]*.

1.3 Any two from: e.g. near to the central business district (CBD) for easy access to banks etc. *[1 mark]* / close to good road and rail links for easy access *[1 mark]* / close to Newcastle International Airport for international travel *[1 mark]* / near to two universities for collaborations with researchers *[1 mark]*.

2.1 North Somerset: 7.4% increase *[1 mark]*
Argyll and Bute: 3.4% decrease *[1 mark]*
For North Somerset, (202 566 − 188 564) ÷ 188 564 × 100 = 7.4%
For Argyll and Bute, (88 166 − 91 306) ÷ 91 306 × 100 = −3.4%

2.2 North Somerset: Any one from: e.g. people may be moving to North Somerset to be nearer motorway and rail links *[1 mark]*. / People may be moving to smaller towns in North Somerset that have easy access to the cities *[1 mark]*.
Argyll and Bute: Any one from: e.g. there could be fewer jobs available *[1 mark]*. / The lack of transport links means the area is quite inaccessible, so it's hard to commute from there to other areas for work *[1 mark]*.

2.3 This question is level marked. How to grade your answer:
Level 0: There is no relevant information. *[0 marks]*
Level 1: There is a basic discussion of the possible impacts of population change. *[1-2 marks]*
Level 2: There is a clear discussion of the possible impacts of population change on North Somerset and Argyll and Bute. *[3-4 marks]*
Here are some points your answer may include:
* The increasing population in North Somerset may cause house prices to rise, pricing out locals; roads in North Somerset may become congested; services like schools may become oversubscribed.
* Decreasing population in Argyll and Bute may lead to a decrease in services; schools, shops and other businesses in some areas may close.

3.1 Any one from: e.g. the houses in the photograph of Bath appear to be larger and grander than those in the photograph of Chadderton *[1 mark]*. / There are several factories in the photograph of Chadderton, whereas the photograph of Bath includes more offices and shops, which usually provide better-paid jobs *[1 mark]*.
You won't get the mark for giving evidence that can't be seen in the photo.

3.2 Any one from: e.g. the growth of post-industrial service industries has mostly benefited the south *[1 mark]*. / The decline of heavy industry has had a greater negative impact on the north of the UK than the south *[1 mark]*.

3.3 This question is level marked. How to grade your answer:
Level 0: There is no relevant information. *[0 marks]*
Level 1: There is a basic explanation of how the north-south divide can be reduced. *[1-2 marks]*
Level 2: There is a clear explanation of how the north-south divide can be reduced. *[3-4 marks]*

Here are some points your answer may include:
* Devolving more powers to Scotland, Wales, Northern Ireland and some local councils in the north of England can help to reduce the development gap by providing money that can be used on schemes they feel will best help the development of the local area.
* Creating Enterprise Zones could help to reduce the north-south divide by encouraging companies to locate in areas of high unemployment, bringing jobs and income to areas that need them.
* The Northern Powerhouse could help reduce the north-south divide by attracting investment into the north and improving transport links between northern cities.
* Transport links between the north and the south of the country could be improved, e.g. the development of the HS2 line, which will allow faster journeys.

4.1 E.g. Links such as the Channel Tunnel make it quick and easy for people to get to and from other countries in Europe *[1 mark]*. Goods can also be transported easily, increasing the UK's potential for trade with other countries *[1 mark]*.

Unit 2C — Resource Management

Page 67: Food in the UK

1.1 There has been a growing demand for seasonal products all year round *[1 mark]*, so fruit and vegetables are being imported from further afield, e.g. strawberries from Spain and apples from New Zealand *[1 mark]*.

1.2 There has been an increase in the number of high-value foods, such as papayas and other exotic fruits, that are imported *[1 mark]*. They have become more popular in the UK as people's incomes have increased *[1 mark]*.

1.3 Transporting food from where it is grown to where it is sold produces greenhouse gases *[1 mark]*. The further the food travels, the more greenhouse gases are produced, so importing apples from New Zealand produces a large quantity of greenhouse gases *[1 mark]*. It therefore contributes more to global warming than sourcing them locally *[1 mark]*.

1.4 Any one from: e.g. farmers markets/farm shops are selling locally grown food *[1 mark]*. / People are buying vegetable boxes containing local produce *[1 mark]*.

1.5 Any one from: e.g. there has been a growth in agribusiness/industrialisation of agriculture *[1 mark]*. This has meant that farm sizes and the amount of chemicals used in food production have been increasing *[1 mark]*. / There has been an increase in the number of organic farms *[1 mark]*, where food is produced according to strict regulations, e.g. artificial fertilisers are banned *[1 mark]*.

Page 68: Managing the UK's Water

1.1 The north and the west of the UK have high rainfall, which means there's a good supply of water *[1 mark]*. The south east and west midlands have high population densities, which means there's a high demand for water *[1 mark]*.

1.2 Cardiff — water surplus *[1 mark]* because it has high annual rainfall and a low regional population density *[1 mark]*.
London — water deficit *[1 mark]* because it has low annual rainfall and a very high regional population density *[1 mark]*.

1.3 This question is level marked. How to grade your answer:
Level 0: There is no relevant information. *[0 marks]*
Level 1: There is at least one reason given for the increasing water deficit with a basic explanation. *[1-2 marks]*
Level 2: There is a range of reasons given for the increasing water deficit in some areas with a detailed explanation. *[3-4 marks]*

Unit 2: Challenges in the Human Environment

Here are some points your answer may include:
- Since 1975, the amount of water used by households in the UK has gone up. This is partly because people have more appliances that use lots of water, e.g. dishwashers and washing machines.
- The UK population is predicted to increase by over 6 million people by 2040, so the demand for water is increasing.
- Population densities are changing. For example, lots of new homes are planned to be built in the south east. There is already a water deficit there, and more homes and more people will increase the deficit.
- Some water is polluted by chemicals being washed off farmland, roads and industrial areas. This water cannot be used until it has been cleaned, so there is less water available. This puts more pressure on water resources, especially in areas with a water deficit.

1.4   Any one from: e.g. improving drainage systems, for example by slowing down the movement of rainwater to rivers *[1 mark]* so that pollutants can be broken down in the soil *[1 mark]*. / Imposing regulations on the amount and types of fertilisers and pesticides used *[1 mark]*, so that excess pollutants aren't washed into water sources *[1 mark]*.

Page 69: Energy in the UK

1.1   coal *[1 mark]*

1.2   gas *[1 mark]*

1.3   E.g. the proportion of energy from coal and oil decreased from 91% in 1970 to 51% in 2014 *[1 mark]*. The proportion of energy from gas increased hugely from 6% in 1970 to 34% in 2014 *[1 mark]*. Between 1970 and 2014 a variety of renewable sources of energy were introduced *[1 mark]*.

1.4   Any one from: e.g. there has been a decline in demand *[1 mark]* due to efforts to reduce CO_2 emissions *[1 mark]*. / Less coal is being mined *[1 mark]* because the cost of mining is increasing as the reserves of coal are decreasing *[1 mark]*.

1.5   Any one from: e.g. the cost to the consumer of electricity from renewable energy sources is relatively high *[1 mark]*. / Research into renewable energy sources and the initial cost of setting up the means of producing them is expensive *[1 mark]*. / Some renewable sources don't provide a reliable supply of energy, so the UK still has to import energy from other countries *[1 mark]*.

1.6   This question is level marked. How to grade your answer:

    Level 0:   There is no relevant information. *[0 marks]*

    Level 1:   There are a few points about the effect of exploiting energy reserves on the environment. *[1-2 marks]*

    Level 2:   There is a basic explanation of the effect of exploiting energy reserves on the environment. *[3-4 marks]*

    Level 3:   There is a detailed explanation of the effect of exploiting energy reserves on the environment. *[5-6 marks]*

Here are some points your answer may include:
- Burning fossil fuels releases carbon dioxide and other greenhouse gases, which contribute to global warming.
- Fracking may pollute groundwater, damaging natural ecosystems. It also causes mini-earthquakes, which could impact local wildlife.
- Accidents, such as oil spills or nuclear disasters, can leak toxic chemicals into water sources, soils and the atmosphere. This affects local ecosystems and may reduce the number of species living in the area.
- Natural ecosystems can be damaged by the installation of renewable energy generators such as tidal barrage systems or large wind farms.
- Power stations and wind farms are often considered to be eyesores because they alter the look of the natural environment.

Unit 2C — Food

Pages 70-71: Global Demand For Food

1.1   E.g: most of the countries that produced less than 2.8 million tonnes of cereals each year are in Africa and the Middle East *[1 mark]*. There are several countries that produced less than 2.8 million tonnes of cereals in South America, and some smaller countries in Europe and Asia *[1 mark]*.

You may also have mentioned that there is a belt of countries producing less than 2.8 million tonnes of cereal running down the centre of Africa from north to south.

1.2   Any two from: e.g. Angola has higher levels of poverty than the USA *[1 mark]*, which means that farmers may not be able to afford pesticides or fertilisers *[1 mark]*. / The USA may be able to afford better technology, e.g. mechanised farm equipment, than Angola *[1 mark]*, which can increase the amount of food that can be grown by making the process more efficient *[1 mark]*. / The USA may be able to afford to use new technologies, e.g. genetic engineering, whereas Angola may be too poor *[1 mark]*. Genetic engineering can be used to protect plants from disease, increase yields and help them cope better with harsh climates *[1 mark]*. / Angola may experience more conflict than the USA *[1 mark]*, which may affect the amount of farming land that is available and safe to use to produce food *[1 mark]*.

2.1   E.g. arid landscapes, such as Namibia, have too little rainfall, which can reduce the amount of food that can be grown because crops and livestock need water to survive *[1 mark]*. High temperatures may increase evaporation, making the area even drier *[1 mark]*.

3.1   C *[1 mark]*

3.2   Food insecurity is when people aren't able to get enough food to stay healthy or lead an active life *[1 mark]*. If daily calorie intake is low, it may indicate that people aren't able to get enough food *[1 mark]*.

3.3   Any two from: e.g. there may be a famine, causing starvation and death, if the lack of food becomes serious *[1 mark]*. / People may experience poor health due to undernutrition *[1 mark]*. / Soil erosion due to unsustainable agricultural practices (e.g. over-cultivation) may increase *[1 mark]*. / Rising food prices due to shortages mean that the poorest can't afford to feed themselves properly *[1 mark]*. / Social unrest caused by food shortages and lack of help from governments *[1 mark]*.

4.1   The risk of food insecurity in the area will probably increase because the arrival of refugees will increase the demand for food *[1 mark]*. Access to food will be difficult for the refugees, who have had to flee their homes and may not have money to buy food *[1 mark]*. The refugees may be forced to rely on handouts like those shown in Figure 4, and the host country may struggle to provide handouts if it is a poor country or if imports have been disrupted because of the conflict *[1 mark]*.

Page 72: Increasing Food Production

1.1   9 million tonnes *[1 mark]*.

Canada produced about 2.8 million tonnes of corn in 1970, and about 11.8 million tonnes in 2010.

1.2   Canada increased its corn production from roughly 1 million tonnes per year in 1961 to about 14 million tonnes per year in 2013 *[1 mark]*. However, there was no overall increase in corn production in Zimbabwe, with production varying between about 0.5 and 3 million tonnes *[1 mark]*.

1.3   Any one from: e.g. improving water supply by using individual wells with easy to maintain, mechanical pumps *[1 mark]* / improving crop irrigation using a drip irrigation system constructed from local materials *[1 mark]*.

Unit 2: Challenges in the Human Environment

1.4 This question is level marked. How to grade your answer:
Level 0: There is no relevant information. *[0 marks]*
Level 1: There is a basic explanation of how new technologies might have increased corn production in Canada. *[1-2 marks]*
Level 2: There is a clear explanation of how new technologies might have increased corn production in Canada. *[3-4 marks]*
Here are some points your answer may include:
- Biotechnology (genetic engineering) could have been used to increase crop yields.
- Biotechnology can also be used to improve resistance to drought, disease or pests so that crop yields are higher.
- Hydroponics or aeroponics could have been used to improve the yield of high value crops.
- Increasing mechanisation and use of fertilisers and pesticides (the Green Revolution) can also increase yields.

1.5 This question is level marked. How to grade your answer:
Level 0: There is no relevant information. *[0 marks]*
Level 1: There is a basic assessment of the success of a named large-scale agricultural development. *[1-2 marks]*
Level 2: There is a clear assessment of the success of a named large-scale agricultural development. *[3-4 marks]*
Your answer must refer to a named example and come to a conclusion about whether the scheme has been successful.
Here are some points your answer may include:
- A brief description of the scheme.
- A discussion of the advantages, e.g. creation of jobs, increasing food security, increasing availability of locally grown produce which can decrease the carbon footprint of food.
- A discussion of the disadvantages, e.g. loss of natural habitats and disruption to ecosystems, displacement of people by dam construction, high costs of the food produced, any ways in which the scheme didn't fulfil its original aims.
- Answers may refer to Burkina Faso, where dams and reservoirs were built to provide a reliable water supply for irrigation, e.g. the Bagrè Dam and Irrigation System.

Page 73: Sustainable Food Supplies

1.1 This question is level marked. How to grade your answer:
Level 0: There is no relevant information. *[0 marks]*
Level 1: There is a basic explanation of the advantages of vertical farming in Singapore. *[1-2 marks]*
Level 2: There is a clear explanation of the advantages of vertical farming in Singapore. *[3-4 marks]*
Level 3: There is a detailed explanation of the advantages of vertical farming in Singapore. *[5-6 marks]*
Here are some points your answer may include:
- Singapore is densely populated and only has 250 acres available for farming. Vertical farming takes up much less space than conventional farming, so more food can be grown in a smaller area.
- Over 90% of Singapore's food is imported. Increasing locally grown crops improves food security because it makes Singapore less reliant on imports, which could be affected by conflict, increasing prices etc.
- Singapore has a monsoon climate that can damage outdoor crops. Growing crops under shelter, as in vertical farming, reduces crops damaged by the weather and so allows food to be grown all year round.
- Vertical farming allows the recycling of water, which means that it is a more sustainable form of agriculture because it doesn't use as many natural resources.

Make sure you refer to Figure 1 in your answer — you're asked to use it in the question and it gives lots of clues about what you should include.

1.2 Any one from: e.g. organic farming uses natural processes that return nutrients to the soil *[1 mark]*. Artificial herbicides and pesticides that are made from unsustainable resources are banned *[1 mark]*. This reduces damage to the environment and means that food can continue to be grown to feed future generations *[1 mark]*. / Permaculture aims to recreate natural ecosystems by e.g. using mixed crops and natural predators to protect the soil, insects and other wildlife *[1 mark]*. It's designed to need low energy inputs and to be long lasting *[1 mark]*. This reduces damage to the environment and doesn't use up as many resources, so food can continue to be grown to feed future generations *[1 mark]*.

1.3 This question is level marked. How to grade your answer:
Level 0: There is no relevant information. *[0 marks]*
Level 1: There is a basic explanation of how a local farming scheme in an LIC or NEE has made food supplies more sustainable. *[1-2 marks]*
Level 2: There is a clear explanation of how a local farming scheme in an LIC or NEE has made food supplies more sustainable. *[3-4 marks]*
Your answer must refer to a specific example.
Here are some points your answer may include:
- A brief description of the scheme.
- How it has made food supplies more sustainable, e.g. by increasing yields and decreasing the amount of resources (e.g. water, fertiliser) needed.
- Other ways in which the scheme is sustainable, e.g. protecting against environmental damage (such as desertification) and preserving the land for future generations.
- Answers may refer to agroforestry schemes in Mali where crops like maize are planted between trees and nitrogen-fixing plants. This reduces the need for fertilisers, helps prevent soil erosion, and increases the nutrient and water content of the soil. As a result, yields are higher and the soil is protected.

Unit 2C — Water

Pages 74-75: Global Demand for Water

1.1 Canada *[1 mark]*
1.2 Mexico *[1 mark]*
1.3 Increased wealth is related to increased water consumption *[1 mark]*.
1.4 Any one from: Mexico has a high population density of 65 people per km^2 *[1 mark]*, so there is not enough water available to meet the needs of the whole population *[1 mark]*. / Mexico has a high average temperature of 21°C *[1 mark]*, so it probably has high rates of evaporation, resulting in the loss of surface water to the atmosphere *[1 mark]*.
1.5 Canada has a low population density, so demand for water is relatively low *[1 mark]*. Although Canada receives less rainfall than the USA or Mexico, the climate there is cooler *[1 mark]*, so less water is lost to evaporation *[1 mark]*.
1.6 This question is level marked. How to grade your answer:
Level 0: There is no relevant information. *[0 marks]*
Level 1: There is a basic explanation of the effect of economic development on the demand for water. *[1-2 marks]*
Level 2: There is a detailed explanation of the effect of economic development on the demand for water. *[3-4 marks]*
Here are some points your answer may include:
- As Mexico becomes more economically developed, it is likely to become more industrialised. Manufacturing uses a lot of water, so water consumption will increase.
- As Mexico develops, people's wealth will increase and they will be able to afford a higher standard of living. This will increase water use, as more people can afford flushing toilets, showers, dishwashers, etc.

Answers

- Both industry and domestic appliances require lots of energy, so Mexico will need to produce more energy as it develops. Lots of water is required to produce energy, e.g. in cooling thermal power plants, so this will also increase water demand.

2.1 Any one from: e.g. the children are collecting water from an open pool, suggesting that there's no piped water supply *[1 mark]*. / The children are collecting water that looks unclean/unsafe to drink *[1 mark]*.

2.2 E.g. the climate looks dry and hot *[1 mark]* so there may not be much rainfall and lots of water may be lost due to evaporation *[1 mark]*.

2.3 Any two from: e.g. population growth increases the amount of water used, which decreases availability *[1 mark]*. / Industry uses a lot of water, so industrial development can decrease water availability *[1 mark]*. / The pollution of water sources, e.g. rivers, lakes and groundwater, can reduce the amount of clean water that is available *[1 mark]*. / Limited infrastructure, e.g. lack of water pipes and sewers, might mean that sewage contaminates the water supply, decreasing water availability *[1 mark]*. / People may not be able to afford to have water supplied to their home and may not have a water source nearby *[1 mark]*.

2.4 E.g. people may become ill from drinking contaminated water *[1 mark]*. / A shortage of water means that less food can be grown, which could lead to starvation *[1 mark]*.

2.5 Manufacturing industries are very water-intensive, so they can't produce as much during water shortages *[1 mark]*. This may force industries to close *[1 mark]*.

2.6 E.g. when countries in areas of water insecurity share the same water supplies *[1 mark]*, water shortages may cause one country to take more water from the shared supplies, leading to conflict *[1 mark]*.

Page 76: Increasing Water Supply

1.1 Rainfall is relatively low all year round (less than 50 mm on average per month) *[1 mark]*. Rainfall generally increases between January and June and is at its lowest levels between July and December *[1 mark]*.

1.2 In Eagleton the population density is high but rainfall is low, so there is likely to be a water deficit *[1 mark]*. In Letsville the population density is lower and rainfall is higher, so it's likely to have a water surplus that could be transferred to Eagleton *[1 mark]*.

1.3 Any one from: e.g. building a dam across the river would trap water behind the dam, creating a reservoir *[1 mark]*. During times of water surplus the reservoir will be filled *[1 mark]*. The water can then be released when there's a water deficit so there can be a constant flow of water *[1 mark]*. / Desalination could be used to remove salt from sea water so that it can be used *[1 mark]*. The seawater can either be heated to evaporate it and then condensed to collect the freshwater, or passed through a special membrane to remove the salt *[1 mark]*. This could be used to provide a reliable supply of water all year round *[1 mark]*.

1.4 This question is level marked. How to grade your answer:
Level 0: There is no relevant information. *[0 marks]*
Level 1: There are a few points about the benefits and problems of the scheme. *[1-2 marks]*
Level 2: There is a basic evaluation of the benefits and problems of the scheme and the answer attempts to draw a conclusion about how successful the scheme was. *[3-4 marks]*
Level 3: There is a detailed evaluation of the benefits and problems of the scheme and the answer comes to a clear conclusion about how successful the scheme was. *[5-6 marks]*

The question asks 'to what extent', so your answer should consider both the benefits and problems of the scheme and come to a conclusion about how successful it was.
Your answer must refer to a named example.
Here are some points your answer may include:
- A brief description of the scheme and why it was necessary.
- A discussion of the benefits of the scheme, e.g. increased water security for the area that the water is being transferred to; increased scope for industrial development, bringing wealth to the area; increased water for agriculture, so more crops can be grown.
- A discussion of any problems that the scheme has caused, e.g. any areas that were flooded to make reservoirs to transfer water from and the effects of this; the cost of constructing pipes, canals etc. to transfer the water; any communities that did not have access to the transferred water; any water insecurity in the area that water is being transferred from.
- Your answer could include details of China's water transfer scheme, which is transferring water from the wetter south to the drier north.

Page 77: Sustainable Water Supplies

1.1 'Grey' water is mostly waste water from people's showers, sinks and washing machines *[1 mark]*. It is relatively clean, so it can be safely used for irrigating gardens or farmland, washing cars and flushing toilets *[1 mark]*. This makes water use more sustainable because less water needs to be extracted from rivers or from groundwater to meet people's needs *[1 mark]*.

1.2 Any one from: e.g. fix leaking pipes and dripping taps to stop water being wasted *[1 mark]*. / Fit dual-flush toilets, as they use less water *[1 mark]*. / Put water-saving devices in the toilet cistern *[1 mark]*. / Buy efficient washing machines and dishwashers and only run them with full loads *[1 mark]*. / Fit water meters so they are aware of their water usage *[1 mark]*. / Take shorter showers and turn off taps when not in use *[1 mark]*.

1.3 Any one from: e.g. the amount of groundwater being extracted can be monitored *[1 mark]* to ensure it is not extracted faster than it is naturally replaced *[1 mark]*. / Farmers can be encouraged to apply less artificial fertiliser and pesticide to farmland *[1 mark]* to prevent groundwater supplies from becoming polluted *[1 mark]*. / Companies which leak toxic industrial waste can be fined *[1 mark]* to discourage them from polluting groundwater supplies *[1 mark]*.

1.4 This question is level marked. How to grade your answer:
Level 0: There is no relevant information. *[0 marks]*
Level 1: There are a few points about how water supply has been made more sustainable. *[1-2 marks]*
Level 2: There is a clear explanation of how water supply has been made more sustainable. *[3-4 marks]*
Level 3: There is a detailed explanation of how water supply has been made more sustainable. *[5-6 marks]*
Your answer must refer to a named example.
Here are some points your answer may include:
- A brief explanation of the water supply problem in the area.
- A description of the scheme and an explanation of how it provides a reliable source of water all year round.
- An explanation of how the scheme has helped to make the water supply sustainable, e.g. how it will continue providing water in the future.
- Your answer may refer to the sand dams being built in the Machakos district of Kenya, which are helping to replenish groundwater reserves and therefore supplying water for the future.

Unit 2: Challenges in the Human Environment

Unit 2C — Energy

Pages 78–79: Global Demand for Energy

1.1   2300 million tonnes *[1 mark]*

1.2   150-199 million tonnes oil equivalent *[1 mark]*

1.3   E.g. the demand for energy in Chile is higher than the energy that it produces *[1 mark]*. Chile consumes 35 million tonnes of oil equivalent per year, but produces only 0-19 million tonnes of oil equivalent per year *[1 mark]*.

You could also mention that Chile has very low oil reserves, which limits its ability to produce energy.

1.4   E.g. Venezuela produces more energy than it consumes *[1 mark]*. It produces 150-199 million tonnes oil equivalent each year, but consumes only 84.3 million tonnes oil equivalent *[1 mark]*.

1.5   This question is level marked. How to grade your answer:

     Level 0:   There is no relevant information. *[0 marks]*

     Level 1:   There is a basic discussion of the possible impacts of energy insecurity. *[1-2 marks]*

     Level 2:   There is a clear discussion of the possible impacts of energy insecurity. *[3-4 marks]*

     Level 3:   There is a detailed discussion of the possible impacts of energy insecurity. *[5-6 marks]*

Here are some points your answer may include:

- Some areas have energy insecurity because they have low reserves of fossil fuels. Limited reserves can lead to the exploitation of reserves in more difficult and environmentally sensitive areas. This increases the cost of producing energy and risks environmental damage.
- Energy shortages can mean that factories have to reduce their energy use (e.g. by only using power at certain times) or relocate to somewhere with better energy security. This can lead to the loss of jobs and of income for the country.
- Energy insecurity can lead to political instability or conflict between countries with energy surplus and countries with an energy deficit, e.g. there has been conflict between Sudan and South Sudan over an oil field on their shared border.
- Without access to electricity, people may burn wood as an alternative fuel. This could lead to local deforestation, which could have environmental impacts, e.g. soil erosion and increased risk of flooding.

2.1   B *[1 mark]* and D *[1 mark]*

2.2   E.g. the USA has a much larger GNI per head than Namibia *[1 mark]*, so people there are likely to own more energy-intensive appliances *[1 mark]*.

You may have also written that there is likely to be more industry in the USA than in Namibia, which uses lots of energy.

2.3   If Namibia's GNI per head increased, its energy consumption would also increase *[1 mark]*. Increased wealth means that people can afford to buy more goods *[1 mark]*. Goods such as cars, fridges and televisions use a lot of energy *[1 mark]*.

Page 80: Increasing Energy Supply

1.1   Location: C *[1 mark]*

Reason: C is exposed on all sides, so turbines will be powered by wind from all directions *[1 mark]*. / It is high up, where winds are stronger *[1 mark]*.

Locations A, B and E are ruled out because they are sheltered by hills, buildings or trees. Location D is ruled out because it is offshore.

1.2   E.g. E would not be suitable for a solar plant because it is in a forest in a valley *[1 mark]*, where trees and the valley sides would block the sunlight *[1 mark]*.

1.3   Any one from: e.g. it's a renewable energy source so it won't run out *[1 mark]*. / Water flow can be adjusted to control the amount of electricity produced *[1 mark]*.

1.4   This question is level marked. How to grade your answer:

     Level 0:   There is no relevant information. *[0 marks]*

     Level 1:   There is a basic discussion of the benefits or costs of extracting a named fossil fuel. *[1-2 marks]*

     Level 2:   There is a clear discussion of the benefits and costs of extracting a named fossil fuel. *[3-4 marks]*

     Level 3:   There is a detailed discussion of the benefits and costs of extracting a named fossil fuel. *[5-6 marks]*

Your answer must refer to a specific fossil fuel.

Here are some points your answer may include:

- A brief description of the fossil fuel and how it is extracted.
- A discussion of the benefits of using it, e.g. it may be a readily available source of energy, it may cause less pollution than other fossil fuels, it may be cheaper than using renewable resources.
- A discussion of the costs of using it, e.g. there is not an unlimited supply of it so it will run out, using it releases greenhouse gases, its extraction may cause environmental damage.
- Answers may refer to the extraction of shale gas by fracking. The UK appears to have large shale gas resources, shale gas is less polluting than coal or oil and is cheaper than some renewables. But extracting it risks polluting groundwater and air, causes small earthquakes, and local people are often against it. Fracking was halted in the UK in 2019 due to safety concerns.

Page 81: Sustainable Energy

1.1   Recreation *[1 mark]*

1.2   0.8 tonnes (accept between 0.75 and 0.85) *[1 mark]*

1.3   Any two from: e.g. insulating walls, roofs and floors *[1 mark]* / fitting a modern, more efficient boiler *[1 mark]* / fitting solar panels to the roof to provide renewable, low-carbon energy *[1 mark]* / fitting more efficient appliances, e.g. energy-efficient washing machines and televisions *[1 mark]* / turning off lights when not in use *[1 mark]*.

1.4   Any one from: e.g. electric cars, vans and trains could be used because they are more energy-efficient than petrol or diesel versions *[1 mark]*. / Hybrid cars, vans and trains could be used that combine diesel and electric power to increase energy efficiency *[1 mark]*. / Devices could be fitted that recover energy lost during braking *[1 mark]*. / More fuel-efficient engines could be fitted in vehicles *[1 mark]*.

1.5   This answer is level marked. How to grade your answer:

     Level 0:   There is no relevant information. *[0 marks]*

     Level 1:   There is a basic explanation of how renewable energy is improving energy security or sustainability. *[1-2 marks]*

     Level 2:   There is a clear explanation of how renewable energy is improving energy security and sustainability. *[3-4 marks]*

     Level 3:   There is a detailed explanation of how renewable energy is improving energy security and sustainability. *[5-6 marks]*

Your answer must refer to a specific example.

Here are some points your answer may include:

- A brief explanation of the energy security problem in the area.
- A description of the scheme.
- An explanation of how the scheme is improving energy security in the area, e.g. by improving the reliability of the energy supply or decreasing the cost of energy.
- An explanation of how the scheme is providing a sustainable energy source, e.g. by using renewable energy sources that limit pollution and environmental damage, and that will not run out and will therefore continue to provide energy in the future.
- Answers might refer to Bihar in India, where 85% of people are not connected to the national grid, and those that are find it unreliable. Waste rice husks are used to power small, local power plants, providing sustainable and reliable power, and providing employment for local people.

Unit 3: Geographical Applications

Unit 3A — Issue Evaluation

Page 85-89: Issue Evaluation — Questions

1.1   280 ppm (accept 270-290 ppm) *[1 mark]*

1.2   B *[1 mark]*

1.3   5 tonnes CO_2 per person (accept 4.5-5.5 tonnes) *[1 mark]*

1.4   This question is level marked. How to grade your answer:

     Level 0:   There is no relevant information. *[0 marks]*

     Level 1:   There is a basic description of changes in temperature and carbon dioxide concentration. *[1-2 marks]*

     Level 2:   There is a clear description of changes in temperature and carbon dioxide concentration. *[3-4 marks]*

Here are some points your answer may include:

- Global temperatures were generally warmer (up to 0.4 °C) than the 1881-1980 average between the years 500 and 1400, then generally cooler by up to 0.4 °C between 1400 and 1900.
- Since 1900, the global average temperature has risen steadily to over 0.5 °C above the 1881-1980 average.
- Carbon dioxide concentration was relatively constant at around 280 parts per million until 1800. Since 1800 it has risen to 360 parts per million.
- Generally, temperature and carbon dioxide concentration followed the same pattern between 1450 and 2000.

1.5   This question is level marked. How to grade your answer:

     Level 0:   There is no relevant information. *[0 marks]*

     Level 1:   There is a basic explanation of why it may be difficult to reduce greenhouse gas emissions. *[1-2 marks]*

     Level 2:   There is a clear explanation of why it may be difficult to reduce greenhouse gas emissions by 40-70%. *[3-4 marks]*

Here are some points your answer may include:

- Reducing greenhouse gas emissions will require social change. This will require people to change their behaviour, e.g. decreasing their energy use or travelling less, which they may be unable or unwilling to do.
- Reducing greenhouse gas emissions will also require technological change. This is likely to be expensive, and it may take time to develop and test.
- Electricity production will need to become nearly emission-free, but most electricity generation is from fossil fuels. Switching to renewable sources would require a lot of investment, which many countries may not be able to afford.
- The IPCC say reducing emissions by 40-70% will also require an overall reduction in energy use, but LICs and NEEs are still developing, which will cause large increases in energy use. This is likely to increase greenhouse gas emissions.

1.6   This question is level marked. How to grade your answer:

     Level 0:   There is no relevant information. *[0 marks]*

     Level 1:   There is a basic discussion of the statement with limited reference to the resource and some use of knowledge. *[1-2 marks]*

     Level 2:   There is a clear discussion of the statement with analysis of the resource and use of knowledge. *[3-4 marks]*

     Level 3:   There is a detailed discussion of the statement with extensive analysis of the resource and appropriate use of knowledge. *[5-6 marks]*

Your answer should come to a clear conclusion on the issue. Here are some points your answer may include:

- High income countries have very large carbon footprints, e.g. in 2011, the USA had a carbon footprint of 17 tonnes CO_2 per person. Carbon dioxide is a greenhouse gas that contributes to climate change.
- High income countries have been more developed for longer than low income countries, so they are responsible for most of the 80 parts per million increase in CO_2 concentration since 1800.
- HICs are beginning to reduce their carbon footprints, e.g. the UK reduced its carbon footprint from 10 to 7 tonnes per person between 1981 and 2011.
- Low income countries and newly emerging economies are rapidly developing, which is increasing their greenhouse gas emissions, e.g. China's carbon footprint quadrupled between 1981 and 2011.
- Deforestation contributes approximately 12% of all CO_2 emitted by human activities, and mainly occurs in LICs and NEEs. However, much of this is to supply HICs with the products they want.
- High carbon footprints in HICs and rapidly expanding carbon footprints in LICs and NEEs means that international cooperation between countries at all levels of development is needed to reduce greenhouse gas emissions and limit climate change.

1.7   This question is level marked. How to grade your answer:

     Level 0:   There is no relevant information. *[0 marks]*

     Level 1:   There is a basic discussion of the statement with limited reference to the figure and some use of knowledge. *[1-2 marks]*

     Level 2:   There is a clear discussion of the statement with analysis of the figure and use of knowledge. *[3-4 marks]*

     Level 3:   There is a detailed discussion of the statement with extensive analysis of the figure and appropriate use of knowledge. *[5-6 marks]*

Your answer should come to a conclusion about whether human activities are the main cause of climate change or not. Here are some points your answer may include:

- The climate changes naturally due to variations in the Earth's orbit, changes in the output of the Sun and volcanic activity.
- Climate change may also be related to changing concentrations of greenhouse gases in the atmosphere, as they trap heat and create a warming effect.
- CO_2 concentration in the atmosphere was almost constant from year 1 to 1800, and then increased rapidly from 280 parts per million in 1800 to 360 parts per million in 2000. This rapid increase coincided with a rapid increase of about 0.7 °C in global temperature over the same period.
- This increase in CO_2 occurred at the same time as humans began to burn large amounts of fossil fuels, which releases greenhouse gases into the atmosphere.
- Deforestation has also been extensive since 1800. Deforestation reduces the amount of CO_2 that is removed from the atmosphere by trees, and if the trees are burnt, CO_2 is added to the atmosphere.
- The evidence suggests that humans have caused the increase in atmospheric CO_2 concentration. This increase coincides with increasing temperature, which may suggest that humans are the main cause of climate change.

2.1   USA *[1 mark]*

The USA has the highest HDI, so it is the most developed.

2.2   D *[1 mark]*

2.3   E.g. countries in the north, north-west and south of Africa are predicted to have a reduction in water supply of up to 49% by 2040 *[1 mark]*. The areas worst affected tend to be near the coast *[1 mark]*.

2.4   Namibia's crop yields are expected to reduce by 21-40% *[1 mark]*. This may be caused by the reduction in water supply of up to 19% predicted for Namibia *[1 mark]*.

Unit 3: Geographical Applications

2.5   E.g. generally, high latitude countries in the northern hemisphere are expected to see an increase in crop yield *[1 mark]*. Southern hemisphere countries, particularly in northern Africa, the Middle East and South America, are expected to see reductions in crop yield *[1 mark]*.

2.6   Most parts of Africa are expected to experience decreases in crop yields *[1 mark]*. This means that there will be less food available in Africa, so food security will decrease *[1 mark]*. The lack of crops to sell will limit income, inhibiting ability to import food and therefore decreasing food security further *[1 mark]*.

2.7   This question is level marked. How to grade your answer:
     Level 0:   There is no relevant information. *[0 marks]*
     Level 1:   There is a basic explanation of why tropical storms affect the USA and Bangladesh differently. *[1-2 marks]*
     Level 2:   There is a clear explanation backed up by evidence of why tropical storms affect the USA and Bangladesh differently. *[3-4 marks]*
     Level 3:   There is a detailed explanation backed up by evidence of why tropical storms affect the USA and Bangladesh differently. *[5-6 marks]*
Here are some points your answer may include:
- The USA and Bangladesh are both in areas that are vulnerable to tropical storms, but the social and economic effects are very different.
- The USA is a high-income country with a GNI of US $55 200. It is very developed — it scores 0.915 on the human development index. Bangladesh is a poorer country with a GNI per head of US $1080. It is less developed — it scores 0.570 in the human development index.
- The USA's higher level of development and greater wealth means it can afford to take steps to prepare for and rapidly respond to tropical storms. Bangladesh is less able to do this because it is poorer and less developed. This means that people are more likely to be killed or injured by a tropical storm of a given severity in Bangladesh than the USA, for example Hurricane Sandy killed 72 people, compared with more than 3000 deaths caused by Cyclone Sidr.
- The USA's higher level of wealth means that tropical storms cause more costly damage there than in Bangladesh. Damage to expensive buildings and disruption to the high income economy mean that costs quickly grow during and after a tropical storm. Bangladesh has a lower level of wealth so damage caused by tropical storms causes less economic damage. For example, Hurricane Sandy caused around US $71 billion of damage, whereas Cyclone Sidr caused US $1.7 billion of damage.

2.8   This question is level marked. How to grade your answer:
     Level 0:   There is no relevant information. *[0 marks]*
     Level 1:   There is a basic view stated and a simple justification. *[1-2 marks]*
     Level 2:   There is a clear view stated and an adequate justification using Figure 2 and other knowledge. *[3-4 marks]*
     Level 3:   There is a clear view stated and a detailed justification using Figure 2 and other knowledge. *[5-6 marks]*
You must decide to what extent you agree that it is the poorest countries that will suffer most from the effects of climate change. Here are some points your answer may include:
- Climate change may cause sea level rise of 1 m by 2100 and 3 m by 2300. This will affect any low-lying country, regardless of wealth.
- However, higher income countries can afford to mitigate the effects, e.g. by building sea defences.

- Models of changing agricultural yield suggest that many southern hemisphere countries will experience decreases in crop yields. While higher income countries such as Australia will be able to afford to import food, lower income countries may not be able to afford this. This will mean that people in these countries may suffer starvation and malnutrition.
- More frequent and more intense tropical storms are likely to cause more deaths and injuries in poorer countries that are less able to afford prediction, planning and protection.
- Changing precipitation patterns and more frequent droughts are likely to affect both wealthy and poorer countries, for example both the USA and Malawi are likely to have a reduced water supply in 2040. Wealthier countries can afford to build infrastructure such as reservoirs and water transfer schemes to reduce the effects of drought, whereas poorer countries cannot afford this, and will therefore be affected more severely. This may limit people's access to safe water in LICs, resulting in an increase in waterborne diseases.

3.1   China *[1 mark]*
China increased the percentage covered by forest by 21.9 − 16.7 = 5.2%.

3.2   The UK, USA and China have seen small increases in percentage forest cover, which may help to limit climate change *[1 mark]*. However, Malawi has seen a significant decrease in forest cover, which is likely to increase climate change *[1 mark]*.

3.3   E.g. improving flood defences in low-lying areas will prevent towns, cities or environmentally important areas from being flooded by sea-level rise *[1 mark]*. By increasing water storage in drought-prone areas, people can ensure a safe supply of water during times of shortage *[1 mark]*. This will help reduce the problems associated with drought, such as failing crops, lack of clean drinking water and health problems caused by drinking dirty water *[1 mark]*.

3.4   Carbon capture and storage removes the CO_2 produced in fossil fuel combustion and stores it underground *[1 mark]*. This means it is not released into the atmosphere, where it could increase the concentration of greenhouse gases and increase warming *[1 mark]*.

3.5   This question is level marked. How to grade your answer:
     Level 0:   There is no relevant information. *[0 marks]*
     Level 1:   There is a basic discussion of whether renewable energy sources are always small-scale and unreliable. *[1-2 marks]*
     Level 2:   There is a clear discussion of whether renewable energy sources are always small-scale and unreliable, which uses evidence from Figure 3 and other knowledge. *[3-4 marks]*
     Level 3:   There is a detailed discussion of whether renewable energy sources are always small-scale and unreliable, which uses evidence from Figure 3 and other knowledge. *[5-6 marks]*
Your answer must come to a conclusion about whether renewable energy sources are always small-scale and unreliable. Here are some points your answer may include:
- Fossil fuels have traditionally supplied most of our energy and are likely to be able to do so for some years yet.
- Renewable energy sources currently produce 22% of the world's electricity. Most (17%) of this is hydropower.
- Hydropower can be reliable and large scale. However, it requires a constant supply of flowing water, so it is not a viable alternative to fossil fuels in all areas. Its viability may also be affected by changing precipitation patterns and water supply.
- Biomass is a reliable renewable energy source that can be used on a large scale, for example in converted coal-fired power stations such as Drax in Yorkshire. However, it requires a constant supply of biomass, which in some cases has to be imported, contributing to greenhouse gas emissions. It may therefore not be a viable alternative to fossil fuels in all areas.

Answers

Unit 3: Geographical Applications

- Wind generates 6% of the UK's electricity, and large offshore windfarms can generate significant amounts of power. But the wind does not always blow, so they are unreliable as they cannot generate electricity all the time.
- Solar is a growing source of renewable energy in the UK, but it is not yet used on a large scale and provides only 0.4% of the UK's electricity needs. It needs quite intense sunlight to produce significant amounts of power, so although it may be a viable alternative to fossil fuels in some countries, it is not suitable for all.

3.6   This question is level marked. There are 3 extra marks available for spelling, punctuation and grammar.
How to grade your answer:
Level 0:   There is no relevant information. *[0 marks]*
Level 1:   There is a basic view stated and a simple justification. *[1-3 marks]*
Level 2:   There is a clear view stated and an adequate justification using at least one figure and other knowledge. *[4-6 marks]*
Level 3:   There is a thorough evaluation of the effectiveness of each scheme at reducing the social, economic and environmental consequences of climate change, and a clear argument for a chosen scheme. The answer draws on evidence from all three figures. *[7-9 marks]*
Make sure your spelling, punctuation and grammar is consistently correct, that your meaning is clear and that you use a range of geographical terms correctly *[0-3 marks]*.
You must use your own knowledge and information from Figures 1-3 to decide which of the schemes you think will best reduce the social, economic and environmental consequences of climate change. You will need to examine the pros and cons of each scheme and produce evidence to support your choice.
Here are some points your answer may include:
- Schemes 1 and 2 aim to reduce the effects of climate change by reducing the CO_2 emissions, which Figure 1 suggests contribute to global warming. The schemes may help to make the effects of climate change on people and the environment less severe, but do not directly help those affected.
- Scheme 3 reduces the effects of climate change by directly helping those worst affected, but does not help to reduce climate change itself.
- Scheme 1 aims to reduce emissions from cars, which would lead to a slower increase in atmospheric greenhouse gases and therefore reduced climate change. It is an international agreement, which means it is likely to reduce emissions in most countries around the world. However, it may make new vehicles more expensive, which may cause economic problems for poorer people and encourage people to keep using older, dirtier vehicles. It also only aims to reduce emissions from cars, not from other major sources.
- Scheme 2 aims to reduce carbon emissions from countries with a large carbon footprint, e.g. the USA, which has a carbon footprint of 17 tonnes per person, by encouraging people to change their behaviour. It aims to reduce emissions from a range of sources, such as homes and transport, and it targets a broader range of sources of emissions than Scheme 1, so it could deliver large reductions in carbon emissions. However, it relies on individuals to make changes, which they may be unable or unwilling to do. By targeting individuals it seems to ignore large sources of emissions, such as industry. It is also aimed at countries that already have a large carbon footprint, so it won't prevent developing countries from expanding their carbon footprints.
- Scheme 3 offers aid to those who are worst affected by climate change so they can overcome its effects. For example, Figure 2 shows that crop yields in countries in northern Africa and southern Asia are expected to decrease significantly, so food packages could be delivered to these areas to help to prevent starvation in the case of crop failure. Also, money could be given to help farmers to install irrigation systems to reduce the effects of water shortage. This aid could be given to countries with a decreasing water supply and with a low GNI that may not otherwise be able to afford irrigation, e.g. Malawi, as shown by Figure 2. However, aid does not offer a long-term, sustainable solution to the problem. The scheme also makes no attempt to reduce climate change, it just reduces some of its effects. Without tackling the underlying causes, some effects may continue to get worse, and will therefore need ever-more aid or funding to mitigate their impacts. In addition, the scheme focuses only on people and makes no attempt to relieve the environmental effects of climate change.

Unit 3B — Fieldwork

Pages 90-95: Fieldwork

1.1   Any one from: e.g. how has urban change affected the rural-urban fringe? *[1 mark]* / What challenges and opportunities are caused by urban change? *[1 mark]* / What social and economic changes have occurred in the UK rural landscape? *[1 mark]*

1.2   Any one from: e.g. residents could be asked to complete questionnaires *[1 mark]* to find out their reasons for moving to the rural-urban fringe *[1 mark]*. / Surveys about people's perceptions of the area could be carried out *[1 mark]* to collect information about green space, the availability of jobs and transport links in the rural-urban fringe *[1 mark]*. / An environmental survey could be completed *[1 mark]* to identify the environmental challenges caused by urban change *[1 mark]*. / A land use survey could be completed *[1 mark]* to provide data on the social and economic changes that have taken place in the area *[1 mark]*. / Pedestrian counts could be taken at key locations *[1 mark]* to look at population movement at different times and identify patterns of commuter movement *[1 mark]*. / Traffic counts could be taken on streets in different parts of the city *[1 mark]*, to look at the problems caused by traffic congestion *[1 mark]*.

1.3   Any one from: e.g. sketch maps could be drawn *[1 mark]* to map the glacial landforms in the area *[1 mark]*. / The velocity of the stream could be measured *[1 mark]* by timing how long it takes a float to travel a certain distance *[1 mark]*. / The cross profile of the stream could be measured *[1 mark]* using a tape measure to measure the width of the channel and a metre ruler to measure the depth at intervals across it *[1 mark]*. / The sediment load of the river could be analysed *[1 mark]* by measuring the size of a sample of pebbles *[1 mark]*.

1.4   Any one from: e.g. weather hazards, for example, being out in the mountains when it's raining, windy, very cold or very hot can be dangerous *[1 mark]*. / Slips and falls are likely because the ground is uneven *[1 mark]*. / Working around water can be dangerous because people can fall in and drown *[1 mark]*.

Unit 3: Geographical Applications

2.1-2.2

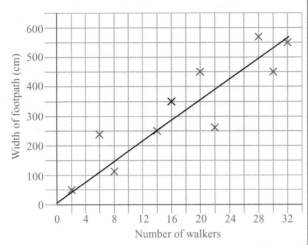

[1 mark for point, 1 mark for line of best fit]

2.3 460 cm (accept 440-480 cm) *[1 mark]*

2.4 Any one from: e.g. it might be difficult to tell exactly where the edge of the footpath is *[1 mark]*, so the widths may not be measured consistently *[1 mark]*. / The metre rule isn't long enough to measure all the way across some paths *[1 mark]*, so there may be inaccuracies in moving it to measure the next section *[1 mark]*.

2.5 Any one from: e.g. repeat the count at each location *[1 mark]* at different times of day *[1 mark]*. / Do more counts *[1 mark]* at different locations/on different footpaths *[1 mark]*.

2.6 Any one from: e.g. an increased number of walkers leads to increased footpath erosion *[1 mark]*. / There is a positive correlation between the number of walkers and the width of the footpath *[1 mark]*.

2.7 Any one from: e.g. the total number of walkers who visit the area in a year *[1 mark]*. / Find out whether any footpath repairs have been carried out recently *[1 mark]*.

3.1-3.2

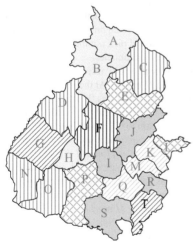

[1 mark for each area shaded correctly]

3.3 21-30% *[1 mark]*

3.4 The north and west of the town has the lowest proportion of houses with solar panels, with less than 20% of the houses having them *[1 mark]*. However, there is an anomaly in District G, where 41-50% of the houses have solar panels even though it is in the west of the town *[1 mark]*. The south and east of the town has a much higher proportion of houses with solar panels, with 21-50% of houses having solar panels *[1 mark]*.

3.5 This question is level marked. How to grade your answer:
Level 0: There is no relevant information. *[0 marks]*
Level 1: There is a basic description of at least one problem and at least one benefit of the choropleth map shown. *[1-2 marks]*

Level 2: There is a detailed evaluation considering both the problems and benefits of the choropleth map shown. *[3-4 marks]*
Here are some points your answer may include:
Benefits
• The data is summarised into districts so the diagram isn't cluttered by too much detail, which might make it difficult to read.
• It is easy to see the patterns in the data.
• The map doesn't take too long to draw.
Problems
• The shading/patterns used for each section can make it difficult to distinguish between the different categories shown on the map.
• It only shows the information at a district scale — there may be variations within each district.
• The groupings for each category are quite broad so it's possible that too much detail has been lost.

3.6 Any one from: e.g. the students could have used a dot map, using identical symbols to show the distribution of houses with solar panels *[1 mark]*. / Proportional symbols could have been used to show the relative number of panels in different areas *[1 mark]*.

4.1

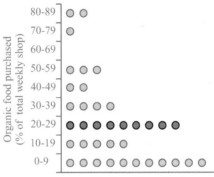

[1 mark]

4.2 0-9% *[1 mark]*

4.3 E.g. most households only buy a small percentage of organic food in their weekly shop *[1 mark]*. 11 households buy less than 10% organic food in their weekly shop, compared to just 2 households that buy 80-89% organic food in their weekly shop *[1 mark]*. More than half of the households surveyed buy less than 30% organic food in their weekly shop *[1 mark]*.

4.4 E.g. the sample was taken from a village with an organic farm shop *[1 mark]*. Local residents may buy food here, so the amount of organic food bought is likely to be higher than in other areas *[1 mark]*.

4.5 Any one from: e.g. people may not know what proportion of their weekly shop is organic *[1 mark]* so their answer may be inaccurate *[1 mark]*. / Fruits and vegetables only grow at certain times of the year, so the amount of organic food available may vary *[1 mark]*. This means that the results may change depending on the time of year that the survey is conducted *[1 mark]*. / The door-to-door survey will only get results from people who are in *[1 mark]*, so the survey will miss off people who are e.g. out at work during the day *[1 mark]*.

4.6 Any one from: e.g. the student could compare the prices *[1 mark]* of similar foods in the organic farm shop and in other shops in the area *[1 mark]*. / The student could collect data about the food miles *[1 mark]* of the produce in the farm shop and in other shops in the area *[1 mark]*. / The student could find out the distance to the various food shops in the area *[1 mark]* and how easy it is for them to get there, e.g. whether they have access to a car *[1 mark]*.

Unit 3: Geographical Applications

5.1 Any two from: e.g. the ranging poles may not have been held straight, affecting the angles recorded *[1 mark]*. / The ranging poles may sink into the sand, affecting the angles recorded *[1 mark]*. / It can be difficult to take accurate readings with a clinometer *[1 mark]*. / It might be difficult to identify the low water mark *[1 mark]*. / The tide will be going in or out during the data collection, changing the point where measuring starts unless all profiles are taken at the same time by different groups *[1 mark]*. / The 5 m interval could include a break of slope, so the results wouldn't show the true profile *[1 mark]*.

5.2 E.g. more cross profiles could have been measured *[1 mark]* at equal intervals along the beach *[1 mark]*.

5.3 Any one from: e.g. the tide may come in and trap people *[1 mark]* leading to a risk of drowning *[1 mark]*. / Working at the coast exposes people to weather hazards *[1 mark]*, for example, people may get too hot or too cold depending on the weather *[1 mark]*. / There can be a danger of people being hurt by falling rocks *[1 mark]* from unstable cliffs *[1 mark]*.

5.4 Any one from: e.g. the frequency of the waves *[1 mark]* / wave height *[1 mark]*

6.1 E.g. **Item:** dog biscuit/orange *[1 mark]*
Reasons: any two from: e.g. they float so you can take measurements from them *[1 mark]*. / They don't have much surface area above the water, so they are less likely to be affected by wind *[1 mark]*. / They biodegrade so the investigation won't harm the environment if the floats aren't caught *[1 mark]*.

6.2 Sample 5 *[1 mark]*

6.3 E.g. the float got caught on something, e.g. a rock as it passed downstream *[1 mark]* so it took much longer for the float to reach the end of the timed section *[1 mark]*.

6.4 255, 278, 279, 297, 302, 310, 315 *[1 mark]*
Median = **297** s *[1 mark]*

6.5
$$\frac{315 + 255 + 278 + 310 + 302 + 279 + 297}{7} = \frac{2036}{7} \;\; [1\ mark]$$
Mean = **291** s (to the nearest second) *[1 mark]*

You may have written your answer to more significant figures — you'll still get a mark as long as it rounds to 291 s.

6.6 E.g. the data could be plotted on a dispersion graph *[1 mark]*.

Pages 96-99: Fieldwork Enquiry

1.1 The techniques you describe should relate to physical geography data that you collected yourself, e.g. beach/river profiles / field sketches / sediment analysis / transects / organism sampling / soil analysis etc. Your answer should give a description of what you did, e.g. sample frequency, method of measurement etc. *[1 mark for each technique described, up to a maximum of 2 marks]*

1.2 Your justification should include why you collected the data and how it helped you answer your original question.
E.g. I analysed pebble size at different points along the river to find out how it changed due to attrition *[1 mark]*. I took a random sample of 10 pebbles at every site to make sure that the data collected was reliable *[1 mark]*. The data showed that pebble size decreased as the distance from the source of the river increased, so I was able to answer my original question *[1 mark]*.

1.3 Any one from: e.g. water hazards, such as drowning *[1 mark]* / weather hazards, for example getting too cold, too hot or sunburnt *[1 mark]* / potential for slips and falls *[1 mark]* / being hit by falling rocks etc. *[1 mark]*.

1.4 Your data presentation technique may be a map, e.g. a landuse map or a dot map; a particular type of chart or graph, e.g. a dispersion graph, pie chart or a scatter graph; or an annotated field sketch or photograph. The strengths could relate to how the variables are presented, the scales used, how the trends and patterns are presented, or how effective they are.

E.g. **Data presentation technique:** pie charts
Strengths: Any two from: e.g. pie charts clearly show the proportion of each class of data investigated *[1 mark]*, so using a pie chart for each place makes it easy to see the patterns between different places *[1 mark]*. / Pie charts allow a large amount of data to be summarised *[1 mark]*, so pie charts make the data easier to understand *[1 mark]*.

1.5 Your answer should suggest an appropriate way of presenting your data that was not mentioned in your answer to question 1.4. *[1 mark]*

1.6 This question is level marked. How to grade your answer:
Level 0: There is no relevant information. *[0 marks]*
Level 1: There is a basic description of at least one technique used and an attempt to support its use in the investigation. *[1-2 marks]*
Level 2: There is a detailed description of at least two techniques used and clear evidence to support their use in the investigation. *[3-4 marks]*
Here are some points your answer may include:
- Measures of average, e.g. mean, median or mode, can be used to summarise the data collected to make it easier to spot patterns and draw conclusions.
- Measures of spread, e.g. range or interquartile range, can be used to show how far the data is spread out or how consistent the results are. This can give an indication of the precision/repeatability of the data.
- Lines of best fit can be used to identify correlation between sets of data and to help draw conclusions about the relationship of one set of data to another.
- Percentage increase and decrease can be used to show how much something has changed over time. They are useful when comparing two data sets with different amounts of data in each, because a percentage shows a proportion rather than an absolute value.
- Calculating percentiles can tell you if a data point is very big or small compared to the rest of the data set.

Try to include specific details about why you used each technique or how it helped you to identify patterns in your data.

1.7 Your answer should describe the patterns in one part of your enquiry, e.g. data you collected on land use, or results of a questionnaire. You should pick out the general trends, include details and identify any anomalies.
E.g. the river velocity generally increased as the distance from the source increased *[1 mark]*. At the first site it was flowing at 0.2 m/s but by the fifth site it was flowing at 1.3 m/s *[1 mark]*. However, there was an anomaly at the fourth site because the velocity decreased again to 0.3 m/s *[1 mark]*.

1.8 Any two from: e.g. the equipment used wasn't appropriate/may have introduced inaccuracies *[1 mark]*. / There weren't enough measurements taken at each site/enough sites investigated *[1 mark]*. / Bias was introduced because of the time of day/location chosen *[1 mark]*. / It was difficult to take the measurements consistently *[1 mark]*.

The answers given here are just ideas for the sorts of things you could write about. In your answer you will need to give more details, e.g. why it was difficult to take consistent measurements.

1.9 This question is level marked. There are 3 extra marks available for spelling, punctuation and grammar.
How to grade your answer:
Level 0: There is no relevant information. *[0 marks]*
Level 1: There is a basic evaluation of the results, but little or no attempt to form a judgement on their effectiveness in providing a conclusion. *[1-3 marks]*
Level 2: There is a clear evaluation of the results of the enquiry and an attempt to make a judgement about their effectiveness in reaching a valid conclusion. *[4-6 marks]*

Unit 3: Geographical Applications

Level 3: There is a detailed evaluation of the results of the enquiry and a clear judgement about their effectiveness in reaching a valid conclusion. *[7-9 marks]*

Make sure your spelling, punctuation and grammar is consistently correct, that your meaning is clear and that you use a range of geographical terms correctly *[0-3 marks]*.

Here are some points your answer may include:
- A description of the results obtained in the investigation.
- The conclusions that could be drawn from the results obtained.
- Whether the conclusions drawn answer the original question of the enquiry.
- Any limitations that may have affected the reliability or accuracy of the results obtained, including the size of the samples used.
- An overall judgement as to whether or not the results enabled valid conclusions to be drawn.

2.1 The technique you describe should relate to human geography data that you collected yourself. You need to describe the technique and then explain why you used it, for example how it helped you to answer your original question and how it provided reliable and accurate data.

Technique: e.g. questionnaires / traffic counts / pedestrian counts / environmental surveys / land use mapping etc.

Description and explanation: e.g. I used an environmental survey, which involved giving a score out of 10 for a range of environmental factors, e.g. litter, at various different sites *[1 mark]*. The survey enabled me to identify areas that were experiencing environmental challenges so that I could assess the impact of urban sprawl on the rural-urban fringe *[1 mark]*. The score sheet I used in the survey meant that the results were numerical, so the data could be easily compared between sites *[1 mark]*.

2.2 Any two from: e.g. walked in single file, facing oncoming traffic to reduce the risk of road traffic accidents *[1 mark]*. / Wore high visibility clothing to reduce the risk of road traffic accidents *[1 mark]*. / Worked in groups of at least three in case of accidents *[1 mark]*. / Wore appropriate clothing for the weather to avoid cold/heat illnesses *[1 mark]*.

2.3 This question is level marked. How to grade your answer:

Level 0: There is no relevant information. *[0 marks]*

Level 1: There is a basic description of at least one data presentation technique used and an attempt to provide evidence to support its use in the investigation. *[1-2 marks]*

Level 2: There is a clear description of at least one data presentation technique used and clear evidence to support its use in the investigation. *[3-4 marks]*

Here are some points your answer may include:
- A description of the technique(s) you used.
- Maps, e.g. landuse maps or dot maps, can be used to show the variation and distribution of the variable you were investigating.
- Land use maps can show the proportion of an area that is devoted to a particular land use. Annotations can be used to explain interesting features.
- Pie charts can be used to show proportions so that different data sets can be compared.
- Scatter graphs can be used to show the correlation between two variables.
- Dispersion graphs can show the variation in a data set.
- Field sketches or photographs can be used to show particular features and add qualitative evidence to quantitative data.
- Desire line maps can be used to show journeys made and distances travelled.

Your answer should be specific to your enquiry — you don't need to include all the information that's given here, just expand on the parts that are relevant to your investigation.

2.4 Your answer should focus on how one set of data you collected links to one of the other sets of data you collected.

E.g. **Data sets**: traffic count and land use map

Links: The traffic was highest in the centre of the town, where there were mainly businesses and office blocks *[1 mark]*. The traffic was lowest along residential streets in the suburbs *[1 mark]*.

2.5 This question is level marked. How to grade your answer:

Level 0: There is no relevant information. *[0 marks]*

Level 1: There is a basic description of at least one data collection technique used and an attempt to explain its limitations. *[1-2 marks]*

Level 2: There is a clear description of at least one data collection technique used and a clear explanation of its limitations. *[3-4 marks]*

Here are some points your answer may include:
- Questionnaires — people may not be honest/may give the answer they think you want, need to ask a lot of people, results may be affected by who you ask and when.
- Transects — choice of transect could be biased, it may be difficult to get a straight line though an urban area, might end up with too many land use categories to be useful.
- Environmental survey — judgement affected by who is completing the survey, might be difficult to remain consistent/not be biased towards the answers that you want, might be bias in choosing the areas to survey, hard to develop a scoring system that covers every site used.

2.6 The data source you choose to write about could be a primary or secondary source. Make sure you explain how it helps to answer your original question.

E.g. I could have used the internet to find data on house prices in different parts of the city *[1 mark]*. This would have helped me determine the social/economic effects of urban regeneration projects *[1 mark]*.

2.7 You need to write about how your data collection methods could have been made more reliable and more accurate.

Any one from: e.g. I could have repeated the environmental survey more times *[1 mark]*, at different times of day and on different days of the week *[1 mark]*. / I could have conducted a pilot questionnaire *[1 mark]*, so that my questions provided enough detail to answer my original question *[1 mark]*. / I could have used a more representative sample *[1 mark]*, to help make my results applicable to the wider population.

2.8 This question is level marked. How to grade your answer:

Level 0: There is no relevant information. *[0 marks]*

Level 1: There are a few points about the effectiveness of the data collection techniques used. *[1-2 marks]*

Level 2: There is a clear evaluation of the effectiveness of the data collection methods used and the answer attempts to come to a conclusion. *[3-4 marks]*

Level 3: There is a detailed evaluation of the effectiveness of the data collection methods used and the answer comes to a clear conclusion. *[5-6 marks]*

Here are some points your answer may include:
- An outline of the data sets collected and the conclusions that could be drawn. Whether these conclusions answered the original question.
- An outline of the limitations of the data collection methods used, and how they may have affected the validity of the conclusion.
- An overall conclusion about the effectiveness of the techniques used in answering the research question.

Answers